A STATE OF THE ART REPORT

DURABILITY OF CLADDING

P. A. Ryan, R. P. Wolstenholme and D. M. Howell

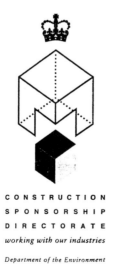

CONSTRUCTION
SPONSORSHIP
DIRECTORATE
working with our industries

Department of the Environment

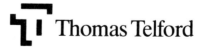

Thomas Telford

Published by Thomas Telford Services Ltd, Thomas Telford House,
1 Heron Quay, London E14 4JD

First published 1994

A catalogue record for this book is available from the British Library

ISBN 0 7277 2012 0

Classification
Availability: Unrestricted
Content: Original research and comment
Status: Refereed
Users: Civil engineers, designers, building operators

This report was produced under contract with the Department of the
Environment. The views expressed are those of the authors and do not
necessarily reflect those of the Department of the Environment or any
other Government Department.

Typeset in Goudy Old Style 11/13.5 pt using Corel Ventura 4.2 at
Thomas Telford Services Ltd.

Printed and bound in Great Britain by The Bath Press, Bath

Acknowledgements

The production of this state of the art report has involved contact with a large number of organisations including manufacturers, contractors, architects, professional bodies, trade organisations, consultants and research bodies. We thank all those who have taken part for their time and effort in making this a worthy exercise, one that we hope will benefit the industry as a whole.

We therefore wish to acknowledge the following organisations:

Alkono
Architectural Advisory Service
  Centre
ASDA Stores
Baco Contracts
Balfour Beatty Building
Booth-Muirie
Briggs Amasco
British Airports Authority
British Gas
British Steel
Building Research Establishment
Butler Building Systems
Centre For Window & Cladding
  Technology
Chapman Taylor Partners
Cladtech Associates
Coma Roofing
Construction Metal Products
Crendon Structures
Crittall Windows
D B Spacey
Ecometal
Enterprise Buildings
European Profiles
Ford Motor Company

GMW Partnership
Grainger Building Services
Greenwood Airvac
HH Robertson (UK)
Hunter Douglas
Industrial Roofing Consultancy
International Paints
Interpon
John Laing – LTG Technical Services
Kingspan Building Products
Laminated Roofing (Southern)
Laminated Supplies Ltd
Metal Cladding & Roofing Manu-
  facturers Association
Metal Constructions Ltd
Michael Wilson Associates
National Federation of Roofing
  Contractors
Nelson Cladding
Paint Research Association
Piers Weston Ltd
Plannja
Precision Metal Forming
Prince Cladding
RAM Building Design
Rolfe Judd

Scott Browrigg & Turner

SFS Stadler Ltd

Sir Robert McAlpine

Sky Roofing

Stoakes Systems Ltd

Stramit Industries (UK)

Syntha Pulvin (UK)

Taywood Engineering

Talfab Cladding Materials

Tesco Stores

Thames Contract Fixing

Tilbury Douglas Construction

Executive summary

WS Atkins were commissioned by the Department of the Environment to carry out a nine month research study into organically coated metal cladding. This state of the art report contains a great deal of new information, gathered as the result of an extensive questionnaire survey on cladding failure, as well as research findings, description of current technology and some practical guidance. The report centres on the durability of coated metal cladding on industrial buildings but also describes and comments on aspects of design and detailing of cladding, life span, maintenance, repair methods, risk of premature failure and problems in use.

Area figures obtained indicate that coated metal cladding forms 17% of the total roof and wall area installed in the UK. Most of this material is profiled steel sheet manufactured by the roll forming process and therefore the report concentrates on this material.

The processes by which profiled metal sheet are manufactured are described together with the most commonly used coatings. The design and detailing of cladding for both roofs and walls is described with sketches showing components, details and methods.

Durability information is presented on over 2000 instances of failure. The data are analysed and presented in graphical and tabular form. Plastisol, the most commonly used coating in the UK, appears to perform well and the incidence of failure within claimed product life is estimated as between 0.25% and 0.5% of area installed. The most common defect is cut edge corrosion for coated metal claddings overall; there is no generally accepted solution for this problem at present. Delamination of the coating was the most common defect for early forms of Plastisol, although later forms showed improved performance in this respect.

The degradation process which coatings typically undergo is described. For Plastisol, information on the number of years to failure for each type of defect is shown graphically. The most common remedial work consists of overpainting in the case of delamination of the coating and painting of cut edges in the case of cut edge corrosion.

A variety of problems in use are discussed including problems related to strength, condensation, fixings and water penetration.

Contents

1. Introduction and terms of reference

1.1 Commission

WS Atkins were commissioned by the Department of the Environment to carry out a nine month research study into organically coated metal cladding. This report is the result of our study and contains information, research findings and practical advice on design and specification. It is written for as wide a readership as possible including: architects, designers, building owners, developers, manufacturers, contractors and those involved in drafting standards.

1.2 Reasons for this study

Coated metal cladding is now used extensively in the UK for a variety of building types including office buildings, business park developments, industrial buildings and agricultural buildings. Associated with this spread of usage there has also been a dramatic increase in the quantities of cladding used both for wall and roof construction. Hence there are a large number of relatively new buildings clad with these materials. Industrial buildings tend to have less individual architectural treatment and more standard construction than office and business park buildings. There have been many instances over recent years where coated metal clad buildings have not met the manufacturers' claims or the owners' expectations. Some coated metal cladding has failed within the first year after construction. It is possible then that a large number of coated metal clad buildings will not be serviceable for their anticipated service life. We have, in this study, endeavoured to gather as much information as possible for the UK to shed light on the potential problems, the reasons for these problems, and their solution.

At present there is some guidance on coating thickness in standards but very little on composition and quality of the coating. Hence there is a need for information in these areas. In addition to this there is little available design guidance and little information on durability, life span, maintenance and repair methods for deteriorating cladding. This program of information gathering, research and study is a step in providing authoritative advice to building designers, developers, contractors and owners in order to enable them to develop better building practice and to deal in the most effective manner with our existing building stock. The recommended further work will help UK competitiveness nationally and overseas.

1.3 Objectives

The objectives of this study are summarised as follows:

(*a*) To produce a state of the art report on durability performance, and problems associated with the use of organically coated metal cladding and composite panels.

(*b*) Utilising the information available and the results of this study, to review the design and detailing of coated metal cladding and currently accepted repair methods.

1.4 Areas of interest

The study covers organically coated metal cladding only. Vitreous enamel coated steel is therefore not included.

Both industrial and office building construction are covered, however, agricultural buildings are not covered. This is because of the more temporary nature of these buildings, the tendency towards 'DIY' construction and the lower grade agricultural products now marketed. To include such buildings would distort the picture with respect to industrial buildings unnecessarily.

Within this study, we have adopted the principle of market share in relation to each particular material or type of cladding. That is, the amount of attention given to each is in relation to its importance in the (UK) market. A recent report (Ref. 1) by the Building Research Establishment (BRE) gives some indication of the market for the various materials. More precise market figures are given later in this Chapter.

The areas of cladding technology and experience included in this study are as follows:

¤   Design and detailing of cladding

¤   Durability

¤   Life span and maintenance

¤   Repair methods

¤   Risk of premature failure

¤   Problems associated with use

1.5 Market size

Some market data are given in the recent BRE report (Ref. 1) on the percentages of the buildings sampled with the various types of cladding coating. This information relates only to roof cladding and only to galvanised steel substrate material. This is shown in Table 1.1.

Coating type	% of buildings
PVDF	5
PVC	83
Acrylic	2
Polyester	1
Powder Coat	1
Unknown	7
None	1
Oil Paint	<1
Galbestos	1

Table 1.1. Coating types used (BRE Ref. 1)

These data seem to indicate a remarkably high percentage of buildings with PVC (largely Plastisol – see Glossary) coated roofs. The buildings here are presumed to be mainly industrial; the report does not state the categories sampled.

Further market figures for 1991 were supplied by the Metal Cladding and Roofing Manufacturers Association. It is noted that the construction industry saw a substantial recession recently and thus the market figures are likely to be low. Figures giving areas of material used in various market sectors are shown in Figures 1.1 and 1.2.

Fig. 1.1. Distribution of wall cladding across the market areas in 1991 (approximate areas in m^2)

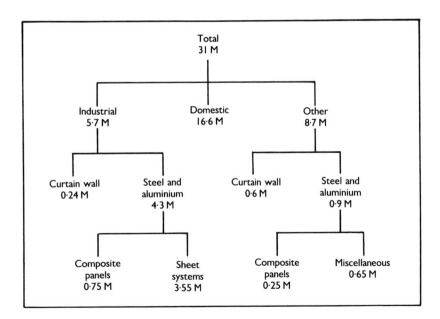

Fig. 1.2. Distribution of pitched roof cladding across the market areas in 1991 (approximate areas in m^2)

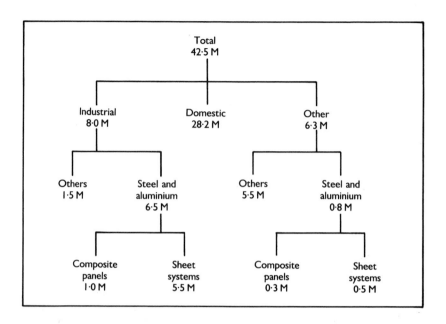

From these figures it can be seen that:

¤ Steel and aluminium roof and wall cladding usage per annum was 12.5Mm^2 forming 17% of the total roof and wall market. The majority of this material is profiled cladding manufactured by the roll forming process described in Chapter 3.

¤ Composite panels at 2.3Mm^2 form 18.4% of the roof and wall cladding market.

¤ Buildings other than industrial, such as business park and office buildings, use 1.7Mm^2 of steel and aluminium cladding which constitutes 13.6% of the total area of steel and aluminium roof and wall cladding.

¤ Curtain wall at 840000m^2 forms 14% of the combined total 6.04Mm^2 for both cladding and curtain wall.

In the ten years to 1991 organically coated profiled metal cladding in excess of 3000Mm^2 was supplied in the UK. This figure covers all coating types and all uses. The predominant coating material used is Plastisol, a PVC coating. The largest producer of Plastisol coated coil in the UK is British Steel and they estimate their share of the UK cladding market for roofs and walls as about 60 – 65%. About 95% of their production for roof and wall cladding is Plastisol coated. Figures are given in Chapter 5 which relate to first, second and third generation formulations (Types 1, 2 and 3).

The amount of coated metal cladding used in curtain walling is difficult to assess. This can be in the form of rainscreen claddings, overcladding or as infill panels in a stick-grid curtain wall. These are more often applied to retail, business park and office buildings rather than industrial. Also, coatings tend to be either a powder coating or PVDF. Information in the NEDO report on Curtain Walling published in 1990 gives market figures for 1989 which suggest that approximately $1Mm^2$ of coated metal cladding was used in curtain walling applications. Comparing this with the figure of $840000m^2$ for 1991 and allowing for a decrease in the market, the 14% figure given above seems to be confirmed.

Generally in this study, cladding types and coatings have been given degrees of importance in line with their usage within the UK as outlined above.

From the figures it is clear that steel and aluminium roll formed profiled cladding is an important material. Usage of composite panel cladding is much lower and usage of cladding of all types in curtain wall facades is even lower. The usage of aluminium cladding in the UK is difficult to assess. Production figures available to the authors indicate that profiled aluminium sheet produced by the roll forming process is only a fraction of profiled steel production.

Usage of other forms of aluminium cladding such as solid sheet, rain screen systems and cassette panel claddings are also shown to be small compared with profiled steel cladding since they too are included within the 14% of all cladding and curtain walling.

Hence, in conclusion, the order of importance of coated metal cladding within the UK related to material usage is as follows:

Profiled steel cladding

Composite panels

Aluminium claddings, including profiled and other forms.

This state of the art report therefore concentrates heavily on the profiled steel cladding materials and their production methods, detailing, durability, repair, risk of failure and problems in use.

Finally, whilst every care has been taken to ensure the accuracy of the information presented, neither WS Atkins nor the Authors can accept liability for failure of claddings selected, designed, detailed or repaired on the basis of this report.

2. Methodology

This chapter describes briefly the way in which information for this study was gathered and analysed.

Three main sources of input data were used :

1. Literature database search. This was carried out through the WS Atkins library and various specialist libraries. The search resulted in over 170 items of literature being obtained. Many more titles exist on database, although these were of less relevance to this work.

2. Information gathering from manufacturers, designers, architects, building owners and others. This was by way of questionnaires. Over 300 were sent out and a response rate of 33% was achieved.

3. In-house research and building information from past projects, studies and testing.

Literature and published information gathered are listed in the References section except where confidentiality precludes this.

The methodology adopted for the study was as follows:

1. Review of the literature available. This involved database search, library search and search at known sources of literature in the UK. Publications and reports were gathered and reviewed for input material to the study or further references. Information from abroad was included where relevant.

2. The initial survey by BRE (Ref. 1) was studied for its input to the project. Further survey work was considered necessary since the BRE report covered only coated galvanised steel roof cladding and the results were not comprehensive enough for the purposes of this study.

3. Information was gathered from manufacturers using a questionnaire. Manufacturers were asked amongst other things for product literature, technical data, test results, product output figures.

4. Information was gathered from designers, consultants, architects, professional and trade organisations using a similar questionnaire to that in 2. above. Information on design and detailing experience with materials and construction, test data, durability problems, repair methods, site practice etc., was gathered.

5. Information was gathered from end users and those with experience of cladding problems and case histories by questionnaires as above. The users included owners, contractors, cladding and building sub-contractors. Information was sought on durability problems, experience with design, testing, maintenance procedures, life span and repair methods.

6. Factory and site visits were made to view processes and selected coated metal cladding repair methods, detailing etc.

7. The literature gathered was entered into a database for easy handling and studied by the authors.

8. The information gathered consisted of questionnaire returns, further papers or documents and blocks of data on durability of claddings. The questionnaire returns and blocks of data were entered into spreadsheets for analysis and output in tables and graphs. In many instances, the failure data were discussed with the respondent to verify or complete the data.

9. An interim report was prepared for review by DoE.

10. A draft final report was prepared and issued to DoE for review. Sections of the draft were also reviewed by bodies within the cladding industry.

11. A final report was produced.

3. Coatings, application and processes

3.1 Preliminary

Understanding of the materials and how they are manufactured is important in gaining an appreciation of coated metal cladding. This is true for those involved in research, testing and investigations into durability as well as for those who design, construct and maintain buildings clad with these materials. This chapter gives a summary of the processes by which coated metal cladding is manufactured. Coatings are referred to by generic type and descriptions are given in the Glossary and in Table 3.1.

3.2 Coil production

The production of organically coated metal cladding involves a large number of different processes and a description follows which deals mainly with profiled metal cladding.

The first stage is to produce the basic material which will form the substrate. This can be aluminium, steel or stainless steel. The production of each of these materials involves complex and sophisticated processes. Each material should be manufactured to meet the specific national production standards. British, French, German and American standards are important in the UK. There is a move towards Euronorms which will standardise the situation across the European Community. Metal arriving at rolling mills in ingot form should comply with the designated national standard for production quality.

The next stage is coil production. Here metal in ingot form is reduced in rolling mills by processes of hot and cold working to produce coils of strip which can be used in the manufacturing process. Temperature control is an essential element in determining the final properties of the coil as material strength is a function of quenching and work hardening during the process as well as alloying of the material. Properties of the final product also depend on the sheet thickness, and variations due to rolling tolerance will influence ultimate capacity. There are a variety of appropriate national standards (in the UK this is BS 2989 which is being replaced by BSEN 10 142 and BSEN 10 147 — see the Appendix for a list of standards) which refer to the quality of strip products. Problems at this

Liquid coatings		Spray applications	
Acrylic	Thermosetting and thermoplastic acrylic co-polymers	Alkyd Amino	Resins derived from natural oils and chemical reacted or cross-linked with amines, brittle coating, thus applied after roll forming
Organasol	Dispersion of PVC resin in plasticiser and solvent. Film formation takes place by fusion during and after solvent evaporation	PVDF (PVF$_2$)	Fluorocarbon, as described under liquid coatings. Formulation can be varied due to different method of application
Plastisol	Thermoplastic containing PVC resin in plasticiser. Formulations are available from various paint companies	Film coatings	
Polyvinylidene Fluoride, PVDF (PVF$_2$)	Developed by Penwalt Corporation, USA and formulated under licence in the UK. Fluorine is introduced into PVC to produce the fluorocarbon	PVC	PVC film applied to the substrate
Polyester and Silicon Modified Polyester	Resins derived from Synthetic materials with Silicon modifications	PVDF	PVDF film. Chemical variations from liquid form produce greater flexibility

Table 3.1. Examples of coating types

stage can occur due to poor quality control or purchase of suspect material from alternative sources. This latter situation can occur with the less reputable suppliers due to pressures of price or delivery demands.

Steel substrates require the protection of galvanising, with either zinc or aluminium/zinc, prior to applications of the paint systems to provide adequate corrosion protection. Early examples of organically coated metal cladding had the paint systems applied either directly to the steel substrate or to an asbestos bituminous coating applied directly to the substrate. Neither system provided adequate corrosion protection on their own. The galvanising is generally achieved by 'hot dipping' the coil after rolling and then re-coiling. The process involves cleaning, fluxing, heating and cooling. The process can be varied to produce different spangle on the sheet which influences the flexibility of the protective coating. The thickness of such coating also influences flexibility and protective qualities. The tolerances are therefore important. There are various standards which cover properties for galvanising with zinc or aluminium/zinc coating. The process can be used to control strength characteristics in addition to coating characteristics by further heat treating the steel.

Aluminium sheets do not normally require a corrosion protection coating, but aluminium sheets which are not to be painted will normally receive some pre-treatment to ensure a consistent finish. Stainless steels are not pre-coated but again special finishes may be required. Stainless steels will corrode in some environments and for profiled materials, a coating formulation which combines strength and malleability must be used.

Thus it can be seen that by the time the coils reach the coil coater for application of the paint finish, the strength characteristics have already been determined.

3.3 Coating types

The next stage in the production of profiled metal cladding is for the coil coater (often a different company) to take the rolled strip metal and apply a paint finish which provides further corrosion protection if already galvanised. Varying types of finish have been used in recent years, falling into the categories of:

¤   Liquid coating

¤   Spray application

¤   Film coatings

Examples of these coatings are given in Table 3.1. Organasol is included for completeness since it is still found on buildings today even though it has effectively gone out of production in the UK. In recent years, the UK market has moved towards two predominant coatings; Plastisol and PVDF (new standard abbreviation for PVF_2 — see Glossary) both applied as liquid coatings by roller. Both materials rely on solvent release in the curing process. The nature of the UK climate has had much to do with the selection of these particular coatings. These generic coating types have been available in the UK for over 20 years but the technology of formulation and application have improved dramatically over that period. Powder coatings now play an important part in the curtain wall market but these systems are not generally used for roll formed products for reasons which include cost and coating flexibility.

Early examples of organically coated metal claddings suffered from a variety of problems including colour change, degradation of coating, chalking, coating breakdown, substrate corrosion and colour batch variations. Some manufacturers recognised the difficulties and sought to overcome the problems in various ways. Prior to recognition of the problems with asbestos and more up to date fire regulations, some manufacturers offered cladding where the galvanised sheet was coated with an asbestos bitumen layer prior to colour coating to give additional corrosion protection. Such products could be successfully roll formed provided the painted strip was not allowed to become too cold. The flexibility of the coating system was temperature sensitive. They were successfully used on a number of major industrial projects. Wise manufacturers limited colour ranges of the various products to avoid bright colours or those where unstable pigments had to be used.

Other manufacturers used well tried paint systems and applied the systems after roll forming the sheets to avoid cracking of the paint film. These systems overcame the problems inherent in roll forming fully finished sheets but limited the rate of production and increased costs. Film coatings, where a film is attached to the substrate by adhesion prior to roll forming, were also used. The advantage here is that the film could be produced to a high quality in controlled conditions, but achieving a good adhesion to the substrate was often a problem and this method is now seldom used.

Most coatings are now liquid applied. After appropriate pre-treatments including cleaning and primer coats, the final coat is applied by roller and, in the case of Plastisol, an embossing pattern is usually applied to dilute the impact of slightly varying gloss levels on an initially high gloss coating. The material is then cured at high temperature at which point the properties of the substrate may also be modified. Figure 3.1 shows the typical coating process.

Coatings can generally be defined as 'thin' or 'thick' coatings. 'Thin' coatings are usually in the range of 25 – 50 microns and include acrylic, PVDF, alkyd, polyester and silicone modified polyester.

With 'thin' coatings, the margin for error in coating of the coil is small; a 2 micron thickness variation could represent a 10% reduction in coating thickness. Advantages of the 'thin' coatings though are generally greater colour fastness, a wider colour range and more consistent gloss levels. Against this must be balanced handling problems (due to lower scratch resistance) and potential damage during the forming process.

Fig. 3.1. The coil coating process

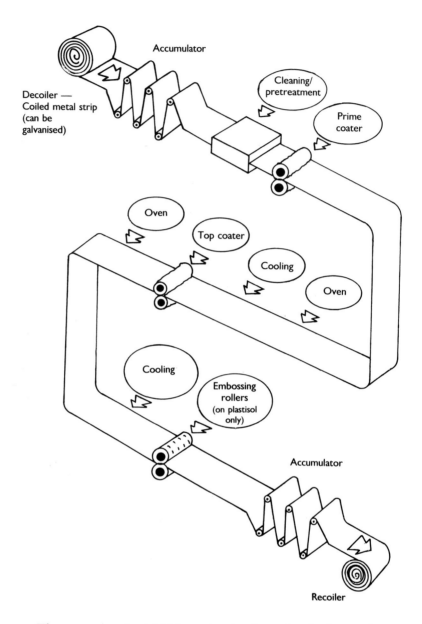

The most popular 'thick' coating is plastisol, which is a thermoplastic containing PVC. In the UK this is available to a nominal thickness of 200 microns. The coating has a 'leather grain' pattern applied during the application process. Coatings of 100 microns can be used for internal applications but do not perform well for external use in the UK. Advantages of the 'thick' coating are ease of handling and tolerance to abuse in use. However, the available colour range is more limited and some colour variation can be expected.

For all coatings, quality control is essential during batching, application and curing. Coating applicators have improved cladding performance by careful selection and monitoring of the coating suppliers. Different formulations will produce different long term colour performance even though initial colour match can be achieved. It is therefore recommended that batches of product from different coating suppliers for a given colour should not be mixed on the same project. The application process must be carefully controlled to ensure that the pre-treatment of the substrate is properly carried out, that dust and dirt are kept off the substrate and that a close tolerance is maintained on the final coating thickness to meet the appropriate quality standards. Curing must be carried out at the correct temperature to ensure that the coating has properly set. With aluminium substrates, care is needed to ensure that the curing process does not alter the properties of the parent metal.

The efforts of manufacturers in the past few years have been towards improving the quality of existing coating types. Improvements must be tested in the laboratory and in production before the refinements are released into the commercial market. Product testing is a complex issue as there are many variables. Natural exposure is often the only real test of performance. More is said about testing in Chapter 5.

Changing legislation and the need to reduce solvent release into the atmosphere mean that manufacturers will need to market new products within the next few years. At the present time there is no clear understanding amongst specifiers and users generally as to what new coatings are being developed, how they have been tested and what performance can be expected in the future.

3.4 Roll forming

The company carrying out roll forming is often distinct from both the strip producer and the coil coater. By the time coils reach the roll former the material has been through many processes, each with its own requirements for careful quality control. In the procurement of profiled metal cladding it is therefore essential to ensure that:

¤ Substrate materials are obtained from a reputable and consistent supply

¤ Coil thickness and properties meet the standards

¤ Pre-treatment meets the standards

¤ Coating application meets the standards

A high quality of roll forming on defective material will not produce a satisfactory end product.

The roll former is near the end of the production chain but plays a very important role in end product performance. Profiles are produced using a roll forming machine such as that shown in Photograph 1 (Chapter 5). The coated coil is passed through various sets of rollers (or stands) on the roll forming machine, each of which deform the coil. If large deformations of the coil are attempted at any single stand, damage can be caused to the coating (and possibly the substrate) as the materials stretch. Hence, the roll forming must be carried out gradually with enough sets of rollers acting on the strip to avoid large deformations at any one stand. Correctly setting the rolls requires considerable skill since any lack of alignment can result in sheets which do not lap accurately and so cannot be properly assembled on site.

Early products were limited to sinusoidal profiles. Developments were then made to produce trapezoidal profiles, and the current range includes deep trough sections with indentations to stiffen both the flange and web.

'Crisp' profiles result in small radius bends in the formed sheets and coating failure can occur at these points. Examples of profiles are shown in Figure 3.2. There are British Standards for the design of cold formed sections including profiled sheets, and shapes vary from simple sinusoidal shapes to deep box sections with indented webs or flanges.

The underside of the external sheet may prove a critical factor in ultimate material performance due to the effects of condensation. This topic is discussed in more detail in Chapter 5 on durability where back peel is noted as a type of failure and in Chapter 8 where condensation is discussed.

3.5 Composite panels

Current Building Regulations require most buildings to be insulated in order to restrict energy lost. Hence, single sheet cladding on its own is rarely used for roofing or wall cladding and some form of multi-component system is usually required. This is normally in one of the following forms:

1. Insulation bonded to metal sheets (not now commonly used)

2. Factory foamed core between two sheets

3. Shaped infill to suit profile, cladding built up on site

4. Separate quilting, cladding built up on site

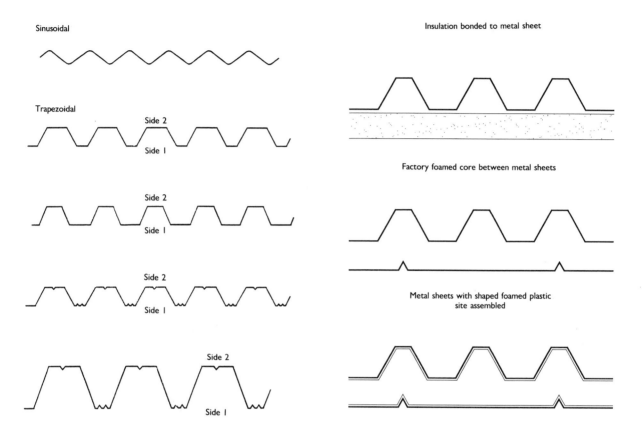

Sinusoidal

Trapezoidal

Side 2

Side 1

Side 2

Side 1

Side 2

Side 1

Side 2

Side 1

Insulation bonded to metal sheet

Factory foamed core between metal sheets

Metal sheets with shaped foamed plastic
site assembled

Fig. 3.2. The coil coating process

Fig. 3.3. Typical composite panel types

The first two types above are composite construction, where this is defined as inner skin, outer skin and insulation bonded together. The last would be as used in a built-up wall or roof design. Composite panels have the big advantage of controlled manufacture and easy site assembly. Both 3. and 4. above hold the possibility of pre-assembly into wall units under factory conditions.

Flat panel systems can also be produced by bonding a flat metal panel to timber or other stiff membrane and fitting the panels within a framework.

Examples of typical forms of construction are shown in Figure 3.3.

There are a number of disadvantages and potential problems with composite panels. Although few of the questionnaire respondents reported problems with composite panels, other experience is that the problems are familiar to many in the industry. Potential problems can be summarised as follows:

¤   De-bonding of skin material from core insulation.

¤   Water penetration through single stage or double seals, particularly when inadequate drainage and/or ventilation is provided in the latter case.

¤   Thermal expansion of outer or inner skin relative to the rest of the panel causing bowing of panels, debonding, blistering or other damage to the panel.

¤   Interstitial condensation where there is no effective inner 'air barrier' causing degradation of materials and finishes.

Specifiers must therefore choose products with proven track record or known, verifiable performance test results. At present there are no agreed standards for testing these products. More is said regarding composite panels in Section 4.6.

4. Design and detailing

4.1 Preliminary

Roll formed profiled metal wall sheeting and roofing is the largest single market in the UK for organically coated metal cladding. This Chapter seeks to outline the design and detailing of profiled sheeting. It is intended to be a summary of the principles involved which will be of use to the designer. Also, in considering the failure of profiled metal cladding it is important to appreciate current norms of design in buildings.

4.2 Profiles

Profiled metal sheeting is manufactured from coated metal strip by the roll forming process which is described in Chapter 3. The process and the rate at which strip is deformed into a profiled sheet is not a precise science but is determined as a result of experience by the plant operators and engineers. The structural design of the final profile is however well understood.

A detailed theory of the structural design of profiles can be found in Refs 12 and 21. These give excellent guidance and explanation. Calculations take account of the stiffening effect that bends in the profile have on the effective crown and valley flange widths assumed in design. The radii of these bends are important since there is a tendency for buckles in a compression flange to extend into the corner regions. Rounding at corners can only be ignored where the inner radius is smaller than 5 t (where t = thickness of metal). It is interesting to note that the effective widths assumed for deflection calculations are not the same as those used in computation of flexural strength. This is because plate elements in compression cannot sustain the yield stress over the whole compression flange due to local buckling, whereas deflection calculations are based on service loads and stresses when buckling does not occur.

In general the greater the distance between supports the deeper the profile required, however longer spans require heavier section purlins with consequent cost implications. Experience has shown that sheet spans between 2 and 3 metres give the best overall economy. Care must however be exercised when glassfibre or PVC rooflights are incorporated into a roof, these materials do not have the same flexural strength as metal and this must be taken into account when determining sheet spans. More is said on this in Chapter 8.

Early profiled steel sheet was manufactured using steel with a yield stress of 250 N/mm^2 but steels with yield stresses up to 550 N/mm^2 are now rolled which allow thinner strip to be used whilst still retaining the same spanning capability for a given profile shape and depth. It is important when specifying a particular steel profile to specify the grade of steel also.

Whilst some roof profiles rolled from thin material can safely support snow and wind loads, the profiles must also be strong enough to support point loads from foot traffic. Sheeting contractors may use proper crawling boards when fixing the original material but subsequent maintenance operatives will not be aware of sheet thicknesses until it is too late and the profile is deformed and damaged as they cross the roof. Experience shows that a minimum thickness of steel of 0.7mm should be used on roofs and 0.5mm on wall claddings. Chapter 8 contains further detail of this problem.

Early profiles, still widely used, were of simple trapezoidal form (see Figure 4.1), these were followed by profiles with stiffeners rolled into the crown and valley which gave enhanced bending performance. Profiles with different depth corrugations have been shown to be very efficient in shedding water from long span low pitch roofs. A further variation is the deep cassette profile (see Figure 4.1) which is stiffened in both directions, this is mainly used for long span decking and allows spans up to 12 metres direct to main frame supports without the need for secondary purlins.

4.3 Fasteners

The success of any roof or cladding system is in large part dependant on the correct selection and fixing of fasteners. Fasteners need to satisfy strength criteria, building design life criteria, building use requirements and be durable under local environment conditions. A fastener should be designed such that under ultimate load it is not the fastener itself which fails but rather the sheet cladding.

Primary fasteners are used to attach metal sheeting to purlins, rails or spacers and must be capable of transmitting all dead, imposed and wind loads to the structure as well as remaining weathertight.

Secondary fasteners attach one sheet to another, to flashings and to cappings. They are used to ensure close contact between sheets and any compressible sealant.

Fig. 4.1. Sheeting profiles

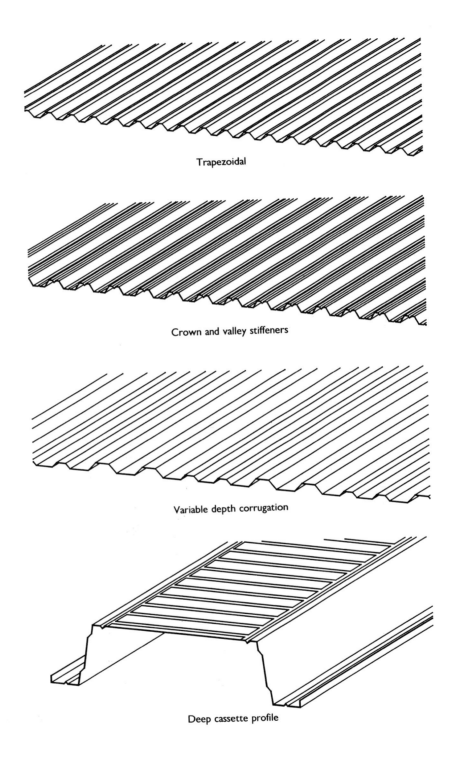

Trapezoidal

Crown and valley stiffeners

Variable depth corrugation

Deep cassette profile

The most popular type of fixing is the self drill/self tap screw (see Figure 4.2). These screws have different thread patterns dependent on the thickness and type of material to be fixed into. The advantage of this type of fastener is that its drill point ensures the correct size hole is drilled to suit the fastener gauge. Where self tapping screws are used, holes have to be drilled as a separate operation, incorrectly sized drill bits can mean oversized holes which will adversely affect the pull-out performance of the fastener. Some manufacturers now provide power tools to install the fixings which remove almost all the potential for operator error. Their use should be recommended in standards and specifications.

Fig. 4.2. Fixing types

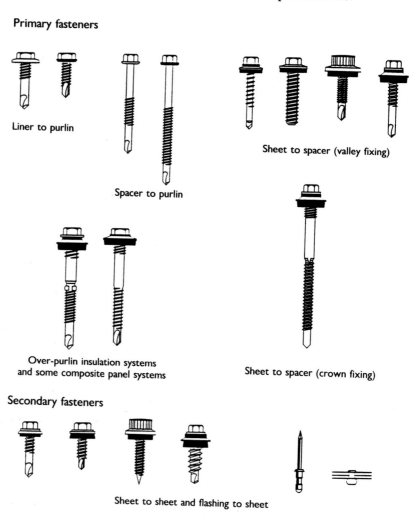

Primary fasteners

Liner to purlin

Spacer to purlin

Sheet to spacer (valley fixing)

Over-purlin insulation systems and some composite panel systems

Sheet to spacer (crown fixing)

Secondary fasteners

Sheet to sheet and flashing to sheet

Fasteners are provided with metal washers suitably sized to prevent fasteners pulling through sheets. It should be noted that larger washers have a greater possibility of inversion under load (see Figure 4.3) and the fastener manufacturers' data should be consulted to determine the correct

Fig. 4.3. Washer inversion under load

Fig. 4.4. Example of sealing washer which provides isolation between fastener shank and washer

washer size. The metal washers also perform the function of compressing sealing washers to ensure a weathertight leak-proof seal. It is important that fixings are not over tightened since this can result in deformation of sealing washers or sheet damage. The materials used for sealing washers must be able to transmit/resist pullover loads, corrosion and ultra-violet radiation. In regard to corrosion it is important that when fixed, the sealing washer has a shoulder which wraps around the metal washer and isolates it from the fastener shank (see Figure 4.4) thus not only providing a weather seal but preventing bi-metallic corrosion between fastener and washer (examples of washers are shown in Figure 4.2).

In order to meet ever increasing standards of thermal insulation greater thicknesses of insulation are being incorporated into roof and cladding constructions. As a result longer fixings are required to secure outer sheets to supporting structure. Special stand-off or spacer type drill screws (see Figure 4.2) are available which incorporate larger diameter threads under the screw head and act as a spacer particularly for composite panels or where rigid foam insulation board is used. These screws provide support for the top sheet under imposed and wind loads and allow the sealing washer to be compressed against the sheet. The different thread pitches are so sized that the rate at which the fastener taps a thread into the supporting structure is compatible with the rate at which it engages the outer sheet, thus maintaining the stand-off distance and not deforming the outer sheet. Some designs provide a notch under the head to prevent stripping the thread cut in the cladding when it comes up against the head.

Drillscrew fasteners are commonly manufactured using carbon steel and have organic coatings, zinc plating or both applied to provide corrosion protection. During installation these coatings can become worn or damaged resulting in a risk of corrosion where the fastener shank is in contact with sheeting or supporting structure. Stainless steel fasteners are available which largely remove the problems of fastener metal corrosion, and bi-metallic corrosion, and should therefore be specified when fixing aluminium sheet. This is because the possibility of galvanic cells forming is reduced due to the relative positions of the two materials in the electro chemical series. It is important to specify the correct type and grade of stainless steel in order to achieve good corrosion resistance as well as strength. There are many different alloys of stainless steel with varying degrees of corrosion resistance and ductility. British Standard 5427 : 1976 recommends that where stainless steel fasteners are specified the steel grade should be Series 300 austenitic.

The use of stainless steel fasteners should also be considered for fixing into timber supporting structure since chemical attack can occur from natural acids in the wood and from some wood treatment chemicals.

Drillscrew heads are available in a variety of different forms, the most common types being hexagon head and bi-hexagon head. Hexagon heads are normally protected from the elements by snap-on plastic caps which are available to match the colour of the cladding. Plastic caps can become dislodged due to thermal, wind or other effects. Bi-hexagon heads are integral colour plastic heads factory moulded to the fastener; these provide a greater degree of corrosion protection.

Drillscrews are fixed using purpose made electric screwguns which have variable speed capability and adjustable fixing head attachments designed to prevent over-tightening of the fasteners.

Drillscrews are also used as secondary fasteners. Two types are available – small diameter drillscrews with fine pitch thread which attempt to tap a thread into the thin gauge sheets and drillscrews with a coarse thread which deforms the sheets into the thread, both fasteners are designed with a small diameter drill point. (See Figure 4.5.)

Fig. 4.5 Side lap fixings

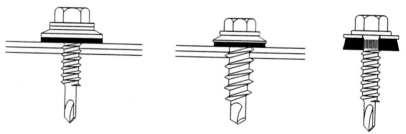

Pop-rivets are often used as secondary fasteners. Specialist rivets which allow adequate expansion under the inner sheet are available for use with aluminium sheets. Washered rivets are available to provide a seal at the outer sheet. It is particularly important to use this type of rivet on roofing. Snap-on plastic colour caps are also available where aesthetics are important.

When using any fixing it is important to ensure that sheet edges are not damaged or deformed during and after construction. In particular, care should be taken to ensure that side lap fasteners hold both sheets together. The edge profile of some sheets can allow the under sheet to be pushed away from the top sheet since they offer inadequate resistance to the drill pressure (see Figure 4.6). This can be overcome by designing more stiffness into the profile to take drill forces or possibly by specifying larger side laps.

Fig. 4.6. Inadequate resistance to drill pressure

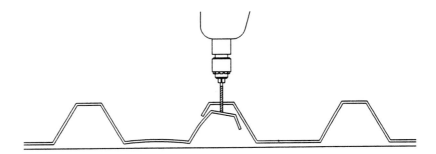

Rooflights are manufactured from glass reinforced plastic or PVC and as such have greater thermal expansion characteristics and are softer than the organically coated metal cladding. Primary fixings are normally standard drillscrews with larger diameter sealing washers which:

(*a*) spread the fastener load over a greater area to allow for the rooflight material being generally weaker, and

(*b*) allow the rooflight to be drilled with an over-sized hole to accommodate thermal expansion and still maintain a weathertight seal.

Notwithstanding the fixings used, rooflights should not be located in areas of high wind uplift, such as the corners or edges of the roof.

Neither drillscrews nor pop-rivets are suitable as secondary side lap fasteners for rooflights. The crown width of profiled sheeting cannot normally accommodate the larger washer size whilst installation of pop rivets tends to fracture the rooflight material and they cannot accommodate thermal movement.

Special rubber sleeved 'cavity' type fixings should be used at side laps. The fixing comprises a rubber sleeve with an integral nut at its base, a fully threaded bolt and weatherseal washer. As the bolt is tightened down the nut draws the rubber sleeve up behind the inner sheet achieving good pull-out resistance.

Profiled sheet manufacturers recommend the spacings for fasteners, but Table 4.1 can be used as a general guide.

4.4 Sealants

A prime function of any sheet cladding is to act as a weather skin and prevent ingress of water. Leakage can occur due to a number of influences acting on rainwater on the outer face of the wall, namely kinetic energy, capillarity, surface tension, air currents, pressure differences and gravity.

Unprotected openings or gaps will allow rain to be driven through the cladding. Small or narrow joints can allow water to be drawn between sheets by capillarity. This on its own is unlikely to be a major cause of leakage, but can lead to degradation of coatings due to prolonged contact with water. However, where wind causes a difference in pressure across a cladding, water entering joints by capillarity can be drawn or forced through and into the building and this is the most important influence on cladding leakage. Much is said on leakage mechanisms in Ref. 26, the AAMA Design Guide Manual for curtain walls.

Roof pitch	Exposure					
	Moderate			Severe		
	Side lap fastener centres mm (max)	End lap mm (min)	Sealant sides and ends	Side lap fastener centres mm (max)	End lap mm (min)	Sealant sides and ends
Over 15°	450	150	No	300	150	No
10°–15°	450	450	Yes	300	150	Yes
Up to 10°	450	225	Yes	300	225	Yes
Translucent (rooflights)						
Over 10°	400	300	Yes	350	300	Yes
Up to 10°	300	300	Yes*	300	300	Yes*
Walls						
	450	100	No	300	150	No

* Provide 2 rows of sealant

Table 4.1. Fixing centres and lap treatment

Profiled metal sheet cladding is basically water-tight by virtue of the side overlap of corrugations and end laps with sufficient overlap between sheets. The efficiency of all joints is in part a function of the degree of exposure and pitch. Vertical cladding rarely requires any additional protection but on roofs, as the pitch reduces so the reliance placed on the sealant joint between lapped sheets increases. Similarly as the degree of exposure increases so does the need for high performance joints.

Sealants used on metal sheeting must have the following properties:

¤ Good adhesion properties and should be applied to clean, dust and grease free surfaces. Specification of workmanship is generally well understood.

¤ Low resistance to compression. Individual sheets are fixed together using fasteners and the sealant should not prevent sheets being drawn together. Typically the sealant is expected to cope with gaps varying between 0 and 4 millimetres. The performance for very thin joints is dependent on the sealant material used but in most cases, with deflection, thermal and building movements, these joints will not be fully watertight. Properly designed joints must limit the movement experienced by the sealant to acceptable limits as recommended by the manufacturer.

¤ Good flexibility. Sealant should easily follow the cladding profile and be able to accommodate extreme movements relative to its thickness, such movement being due to deflection under load, building movement and expansion. Flexibility should be maintained throughout the design life of the cladding.

¤ Resistance to extremes of temperature. Sealant must continue to perform over a wide range of temperature. Metal sheet claddings can achieve relatively high and relatively low temperatures compared with many other building materials due to their low thermal mass and consequent susceptibility to solar gain and night time loss of heat. Large thermal movements will therefore occur, particularly at end laps. Aluminium has a coefficient of thermal expansion twice that of steel which should be taken into account in the design of sealant joints. More is said on thermal movement in Chapter 8.

¤ Capability to be drilled without displacement or twisting is important, particularly with compressible foam strips although ideally drilling through seals should not occur.

¤ The design life of any sealant should be equal to that of the cladding since any system is only as effective as its weakest link. This can only be achieved by careful design of the sealant joint and careful selection of the sealant material.

4.4.1 Sealant types

End and side lap sealants are generally:

¤ Gun grade sealants

¤ Pre-formed sealant tape (mastic sealant on peel-off paper tape)

¤ Compressible foam strips

A wide range of gun grade sealants are available, each with varying proportions of filler and specifiers should ensure correct selection of a sealant which will not lose its properties prematurely. Oleoresinous air drying types should not be used, nor should chemical curing sealants such as polysulphide.

Typically, at least 20% compression is required to ensure an effective seal when using pre-formed tape. Foam strips need at least 30% compression and for this reason are commonly used at side laps rather than end laps. Variations in joint width at end laps will not always allow the full compression of foam strip sealant.

4.4.2 Sealant location

Sealants should be applied adjacent to or along the line of sheet fasteners at side and end laps dependent on the type of sealant. Where sealant is placed adjacent to the line of fixings it should be on the weather or external side to preclude rainwater reaching the fixing. (See Figure 4.7.) This may then trap condensation running down the underside of roof sheets. If condensation is likely the designer must consider the limitations of the simple sealing methods normally used.

4.5 Foam fillers

Where profiled cladding is joined to flat trims, gaps occur at corrugations. In order to prevent ingress of rain or snow, filler pieces manufactured from rubber or polyethylene foam or mineral wool fibre are introduced. The fillers also prevent bird and rodent entry.

In certain circumstances fire regulations may require filler pieces to be manufactured from fire retardant material or, where acting as a fire stop, non-combustible material.

Low roof pitches may require that sealant is provided to both outer and inner surfaces of the filler in order to provide a weatherproof joint. The manufacturers of some profiled sheeting provide special tools to crank sheet ends up or down to afford additional protection whilst other systems provide ridge or apex trims cut and bent to suit the sheet profile.

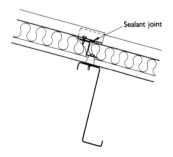

It is often necessary to ventilate cavities within roof or side cladding, for example as part of interstitial condensation control. In these cases foam fillers may have small, say 10mm diameter, holes fitted with fine mesh screens to act as insect barriers whilst allowing a flow of air, alternatively the filler may be cut back to provide a gap, say 6mm, at the corrugation crown.

Fig. 4.7. Location of sealant

Fillers should be positioned such that sheet and flashing fasteners ensure positive location of the fillers. Locating fillers by simple push-fit after fixing of sheeting/trims should be avoided since such fillers are liable to become dislodged or fall out. Where sheet/trim fasteners are drilled through the fillers care will be needed on site to avoid the fillers twisting around the fastener. Fillers are available with adhesive tape or pads to facilitate location and fixing.

4.6 Secret fix systems

Any opening or penetration through a roofing system provides a potential path for rainwater to enter the building. Perhaps the most obvious penetration through conventional profiled sheet roofing is the fixings. A common factor in all standing seam or secret-fix systems is that the attachment does not result in an exposed penetration fixing.

A halter is an extruded aluminium bracket which acts as both spacer, to accommodate thermal insulation, and anchorage against wind uplift. Halters are generally used on roofs where a structural deck without secondary purlins is used. (See Figure 4.8.)

Fig. 4.8. Secret fix attachment methods

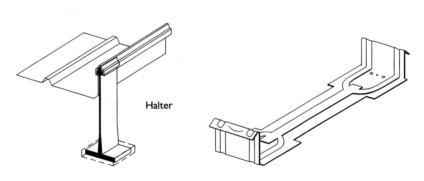

Halter

A clip is a bracket of aluminium or steel which attaches up to three ribs to a separate spacer system or to the structure. (See Figure 4.8.)

Both systems accommodate thermal movement of the weather sheet by allowing sliding, either between sheet and clip/halter or within the clip itself (see Figure 4.9). Typically a roof is anchored at only one point, either ridge or eaves, which allows sheeting to expand at the free end, thus expansion or contraction forces are minimised and are not transferred into the structure. Unusual roof shapes pose special problems in this regard and require careful design.

Although secret fix systems can be end lapped it is more usual to use long sheet lengths. Lengths of profiled sheet up to 40 metres long can be delivered to site (subject to road and site access), alternatively some manufacturers have the facility to send portable roll formers to site.

Longer sheet lengths mean that many roof slopes can be covered without end lap joints. The absence of end laps in turn means that lower roof pitches can be achieved. Falls down to one degree are quoted by system manufacturers, however particular attention must be paid to ridge weathering, and the danger of ponding which could occur when deflection combines with adverse construction tolerances.

Fig. 4.9. Thermal movement fixing

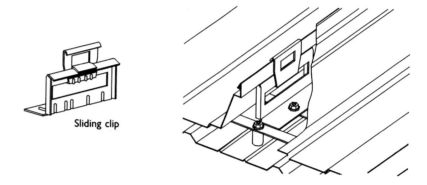

Sliding clip

Where the sheeting is dressed into a gutter, there will be a tendency with low pitch roofs for rainwater to run back under the sheet. To give a better run off shape the ends of the sheets can be turned down using purpose made roofing pliers, or alternatively by fixing a drip angle at the sheet end (see Figure 4.10). Care is required on site with both methods as, with the former, incorrect use of the pliers can damage the coating, and, with the latter, proper installation of sealants and fixings is necessary to avoid water ingress by capillary action between sheet and flashing. Similar use of roofing pliers at the ridge enables the sheet to be turned up to form a baffle or barrier to prevent any rainwater or snow driven past the foam fillers from entering the building.

Fig. 4.10. Eaves detail

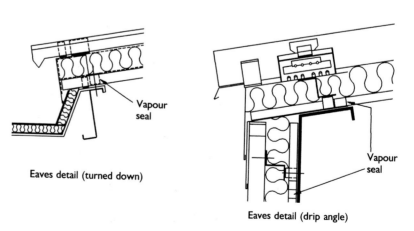

Eaves detail (turned down)

Vapour seal

Eaves detail (drip angle)

Vapour seal

The method of achieving a side lap or standing seam to fix adjacent sheets varies with the sheeting supplier. Systems, as illustrated in Figure 4.11, can include:

¤ Spring snap laps

¤ Mechanically seamed laps

¤ Batten caps over butt joints

¤ Panels engaged and rotated through 90°

Fig. 4.11. Secret fix for lap types (mechanical seam not shown)

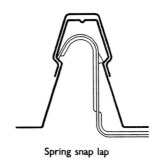

Spring snap lap

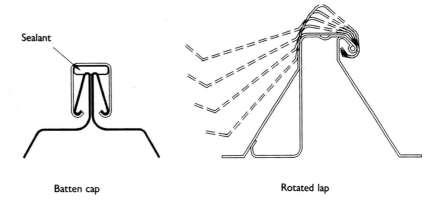

Sealant

Batten cap

Rotated lap

4.7 Insulation

Insulated cladding constructions can be achieved on site by fixing the individual elements – lining boards or sheets, insulation, spacers and the weather sheet. Alternatively, profiled metal sheeting can be supplied to site with insulation bonded to it or composite panels consisting of a metal liner and weather sheet with foam insulation filling the cavity between the two.

The types of insulation available divide broadly into three categories – quilts, semi-rigid batts and rigid boards. Quilts and semi-rigid batts are manufactured using mineral fibres, either rock or glass, whilst rigid boards are typically rigid urethane or polystyrene.

Where quilts are used the inner and outer sheets are spaced apart by a non-combustible spacer, often a metal Z or top-hat section, fixed through the inner sheet direct to the supporting structure whilst the weather sheet is fixed to the spacer. If the whole of the cavity is not filled there is the potential for condensation to occur. Therefore, the cavity should be ventilated and a breather membrane stretched over the spacers to prevent any condensate from the weather sheet draining into the insulation. Examples of insulated constructions appear in the Appendix.

Quilts used in vertical cladding should be properly supported. It is not unknown for quilts to tear under their own self weight when only fixed at side rail positions, particularly when condensation has occurred making the insulation many times heavier.

The Building Regulations require that any cavity within a roof or side cladding has a fire/smoke barrier fitted every 20 metres. The inconvenience of fitting barriers can be avoided where both surfaces of the insulation have a surface spread of flame of Class 0 or 1 and are in contact with the inner and outer sheets. The small cavities within the profile ribs can be ignored. Having insulation in contact with both surfaces also reduces the risk of condensation by restricting air spaces only to the ribs.

Rigid board insulation is available with pre-finished interior surfaces and has the capacity to span between purlins or side rails so that separate lining boards are not needed.

Board insulation manufactured from rigid urethanes (generally a polyisocyanurate, modified polyurethane) or from polystyrene is available. The fire properties and the toxic nature of the smoke produced should be considered when using these boards.

Composite panels are available where the insulation is injected between inner and outer steel or aluminium sheets. The fire hazard with these panels is small despite the use of foam cores because the sheets prevent oxygen reaching the foam. However, in the case of polyurethane, once the temperature of the sheets reaches about 200°C adhesion at the foam/sheet interface is lost and at about 300°C the foam gives off smoke.

Composite panels are supplied with either flat, lightly profiled or profiled inner and outer sheets. The foam core gives flexural stiffness to the panel but this should not be relied upon when using flat or lightly profiled sheets in roofing applications, particularly with low roof pitches, because of the tendency for the foam core to creep.

The insulation properties of the foam core mean that the external sheet can reach high temperatures which the adhesion of foam to sheet must be able to accommodate. The temperature range to be considered in the UK is -25°C to 80°C (see Table 8.1). The temperature difference between inner and outer sheets can lead to thermal bowing of the panel which should be taken account of in the panel design by ensuring adequate rigidity of the sheets, bond strength and stiffness of the panel as a whole.

The panel design will also take account of:

¤ the potential for flat or lightly profiled sheet surfaces to buckle in flexure,

¤ the shear capacity of the core to ensure composite action in flexure,

¤ the resistance of the core material to crushing.

Little information is available on blistering (see Glossary), which is a random problem whereby local areas of the external sheet debond from the core. It can be the result of gas pressure arising from the chemical reaction of the foam cure. A pocket of gas collects behind the sheet and is subject to expansion with temperature. The incidence is related to product design and the level of quality control maintained by the manufacturer.

4.8 Pipe and duct soakers

Any perforation through cladding or roofing to accommodate piped services, extract ducts or ventilators can prevent the free drainage of rainwater. Where profiled metal cladding is used ducts can obstruct several corrugations and in order to channel water around the obstruction a soaker is built into the construction. (See Figure 4.12.)

Soakers can be:

¤ Purpose made sheets incorporating an upstand or collar to suit the duct size with a channel moulded into the soaker sheet to direct water around the duct to prevent ponding. Soaker sheets are made to match the cladding profile and span between purlins or rails where they lap with the cladding. They are usually made of glass reinforced plastic and match the cladding colour.

Fig. 4.12. Examples of soakers

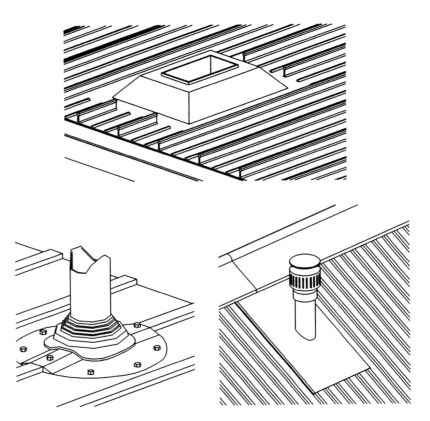

¤ Soaker trays are flat sheets which overlay roof or cladding sheets and provide a flat surface above the perforating duct or pipe. Roof or side cladding is completed and an opening cut to suit the pipe/duct. A flat sheet, normally the same material as the cladding, incorporating an upstand kerb to suit the duct/pipe overlays the cladding and is continued up to the ridge (roof) or eaves (wall) trim. Roof openings close to the ridge (or in a wall close to the eaves) are easier to flash.

¤ Small openings can be flashed using proprietary flexible collars (e.g. Dektite pipe flashings). Rubber cone shaped sleeves are cut on site to form a tight fit around the pipe/duct. A malleable metal reinforced collar at the base of the cone is moulded to the cladding profile and a seal achieved using a flexible sealant.

The number of openings through any roof or cladding should be kept to a minimum and the position of openings coordinated to avoid overlap of soakers.

All pipes and ducts should be supported off the structural frame and not the roof or side cladding.

Examples of soakers are given in Figure 4.12.

4.9 Flashings

Where areas of cladding change shape or direction or terminate, for example at eaves of a building or at openings, a flashing is introduced to weather the junction. Many manufacturers produce a range of standard flashings to complement their range of cladding profiles. Whilst these flashings can be utilised in many recurring situations there will always be a need for 'one-off' purpose made flashings.

Flashings are unlikely to be fabricated out of material less than 0.7mm thickness.

They are also unlikely to be roll formed since their section is not always compatible with such a process nor are they required in sufficient quantities for roll forming to be economic. Flashings are normally pressed and as such the length of flashing is dependent upon the brake-press capacity and dimensions, typically flashings are supplied between 1.8 metres and 4.0 metres in length.

Regardless of how robust and aesthetically pleasing a cladding profile is, if the flashings do not provide a good clean geometric shape and line the overall impression is one of poor quality. Flashings should be easily jointed, either by overlapping or preferably using a butt joint with a backing plate or butt joint strap behind the joint. Flashings should have a stiffened edge to ensure a crisp line to the finished construction and examples are given in Figure 4.13.

Fig. 4.13. Stiffened edges to flashings

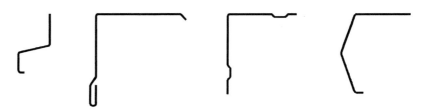

Where flashings intersect, the detail of how the joint is to be formed should be properly thought out at the design stage and not be left to the sheeting contractor on site. Consideration should be given to fabricating junction pieces in the factory.

4.10 Acoustic performance

Sound attenuation will often be required of a cladding, either to ensure that a particular process noise from within a building does not affect neighbouring properties or, more usually, to stop noise from external sources entering the building.

External sources of sound can include aircraft, trains, road traffic or rain, hail or wind. There is therefore, a wide range of frequencies and intensity of sound to be considered, the decibel scale is logarithmic which means that sound intensity doubles for every 3 decibel increase, thus 100 decibels is over 1 million times greater in intensity that 40 decibels. To put this into perspective, a 100 decibel (dB) rating is equivalent to being near an express train whilst 40dB is typical of the inside of a suburban home.

In general, sound waves are readily dampened by heavy construction walls and roof although attenuation varies with frequency. However, for light-weight cladding sound reductions are achieved by of virtue air spaces, sound absorbent materials and sound reflection. Theoretical predictions are possible but these refer to specific constructions and any windows or openings in a wall will dramatically lower its overall sound insulation capability. For example, if an area of only 10% single glazing is introduced into a wall cladding with a sound insulation rating of 50dB, the overall sound reduction drops to 30dB. Further examples can be found in BS 8200 : 1985, for the design of non-loadbearing external vertical enclosures of buildings, there are however no mandatory regulations requiring specified levels of acoustic insulation.

Noise from rain or hail is unlikely to be a problem in most industrial buildings where the general background noise level is relatively high. Similarly, noise generated by thermal movements of a cladding tends to go unnoticed except perhaps in office or showroom situations. Such noise is likely to occur where foil faced loose board insulation is in contact with the other weather sheet which expands or contracts differentially to the insulation. The resulting noise as the sheet attempts to slide over the insulation is magnified in the roof diaphragm and can be a cause of concern for the building occupants. The introduction of an air space between insulation and sheet readily overcomes the problem or alternatively a quilt type insulation could be considered. Care must be taken however that any air space does not create condensation problems.

4.11 Chapter references

Some useful references relating to the design and detailing issues discussed in this chapter are listed below

References: 4, 7, 11, 14, 15, 16, 19, 21, 22, 23.

5. Durability, maintenance and lifespan

5.1 Preliminary

Organically coated metal cladding has to satisfy a number of different criteria in service. The first requirement is to provide a weathertight envelope that provides a suitable internal environment. Secondly, the system must be sufficiently durable to resist external or internal damage to the envelope. Thirdly, the system must resist corrosion to the substrate metal either on the external or internal face of the cladding. Fourthly, the external coating must meet aesthetic requirements of colour and appearance.

Failure in any one of these four categories will lead to dissatisfaction on the part of the building owner, and this Chapter reviews the issues of durability, maintenance and life span.

5.2 Lifespan

The lifespan of the cladding will depend on the coating, the substrate, the environmental conditions and the degree of maintenance. When inappropriate materials are selected, premature failure is almost inevitable and is the fault of poor product selection rather than unsatisfactory product performance. The lifespan required from material for an agricultural barn is different from that required for a quality office development.

BS 5427, Code of Practice for Performance and Loading Criteria for Profiled Sheeting in Building, Clause 19, gives a useful definition of terms as follows:

Short Life Requirement	1 – 5 years to first maintenance
Medium Life Requirement	5 – 10 years to first maintenance
Long Life Requirement	10 – 20 years to first maintenance
Very Long Life Requirement	20 – 50 years to first maintenance

The general definition of period to first maintenance is the time at which the protective system would break down and no longer protect the substrate or when the appearance of the cladding would be no longer 'aesthetically pleasing'.

Evaluation of when the coating fails to satisfy the criteria for substrate protection is a matter of factual analysis. The samples of the material can be removed and sent to a laboratory for chemical and physical examination. Aesthetic considerations are more difficult to evaluate. Even colour fade or gloss loss may be quite acceptable to one user but be unacceptable to another. The ability to detect slight variations in colour varies from one human being to another, making the evaluation even more subjective.

Determining the appropriate lifespan requirement for the product is an essential pre-requisite to selection. Unfortunately, this aspect is often overlooked and therefore the recording of premature product failure could be an inappropriate indictment of the material. In recent times some specifiers have expected totally unrealistic lifespans from materials produced for relatively low cost applications for industrial buildings. Within the context of mass produced products with a relatively low cost base the expectation for a guaranteed life to first maintenance of much over 20 years is unrealistic. Whilst the products may perform satisfactorily for well in excess of this time, given the appropriate external and internal environment and a suitable maintenance policy, it is unlikely that any manufacturer will provide anything other than a heavily qualified warranty to cover periods of over 20 years.

5.3 Durability

The British Standard mentioned above, BS 5427, also covers durability and a classification of external and internal environments into six categories in Clause 19. These are:

External	Coastal Environment
	Industrial and Urban Environment
	Rural and Suburban Environment
Internal	Wet (and possibly polluted)
	Dry (unpolluted)
	Inaccessible (enclosed in cavity)

The external environments are described in greater detail in the Standard but it should be noted that the environmental categories given vary from those given in BS 5493 which covers protective coatings for steel structures. Much of the data from exposure samples and building evaluation suggest that many of the coating systems are not as sensitive to the external environmental categories specified as was originally thought. There are, however, major variations in performance between the UK and certain of the EEC countries due to differences in UV concentrations, humidity and temperature range. Any move to Euronorms needs to recognise climatic variations between the countries.

Further factors in assessing the environment are consideration of future growth patterns, local agricultural activity and changes of use for the building. Future growth may lead to increased or decreased industrial activity with resulting changes to the level of sulphur dioxide and other chemical fall out in the atmosphere. Changed agricultural use may lead to increased crop spraying which may deposit nitrates and other chemicals on the clad areas. Different uses of the building may alter the internal environment considerably leading to other durability problems.

In a changing world, evaluating the appropriate environment for a period some time in the future presents real problems and the careful specifier will undoubtedly err on the side of caution. Advice on the selection of appropriate generic coatings for a given environment is given in the draft of BS 5427 but this needs to be viewed with caution. The advice given does not recognise either current product formulations or variations which may occur to product life from varying parameters such as colour. Certain of the recommendations for coating selection conflict with evidence from exposure tests.

Failure of the cladding may be due to internal factors. Corrosive industrial processes may cause the breakdown of the paint system on the inside of the sheet which may result in degradation of the substrate. Corrosion can also occur at the lap joints in the sheets due to the ingress of moisture or contaminants. In certain circumstances, the internal paint system needs to be of as high quality as that applied to the exterior.

5.4 Evaluation of product performance

Evaluation of likely product performance can be determined from consideration of the following:

¤   Physical Testing

¤   Accelerated Testing

¤   Natural Weathering

In the case of accelerated testing and natural weathering, it is essential that the tests are performed on pre-formed samples. The process of forming a profile causes considerable strain to in the material which can produce potential weakness. Figure 5.16 shows an example of the change in coating thickness during profiling.

5.4.1 Physical testing

The typical tests include the following:

Coating thickness.   Here the thickness of the paint applied to the substrate is measured. There are various methods for carrying this out and ASTM D1400 gives two such methods. The thickness should be measured at various locations across the sheet to obtain the mean thickness and a minimum value. It should be noted that for coated claddings dry film thickness is measured. Care must be taken to ensure that the measurement is for the paint film thickness only and not for the galvanising or aluminium-zinc coating in addition. With Plastisol which has a 'leathergrain' pattern, measurements for two conditions are needed.

Chalking resistance.   Chalking of the coating occurs due to exposure to the atmosphere and to UV light, ASTM D659 gives a comparative method of evaluation by using light and dark felt samples rubbed on the coating which can be compared with photographic standards. The test can be used on samples subject to natural exposure or accelerated tests but care must be taken to differentiate between dirt and chalking.

Colour performance.   Various tests are available and the grey scale to BS 2662 is the simplest. This compares the change in colour between one sample and another to changes in shade of grey of a sample. More sophisticated test equipment can be used such as a spectro photometer to carry out an analytical analysis but such equipment cannot be readily used in the field. Since evaluation of colour variation is as much subjective as analytical, the grey scale with a visual descriptive is an adequate method of classification.

Abrasion resistance.   The two most popular methods of measuring abrasion resistance are the Taber wheel to ASTM D4060 and the falling sand test to ASTM D968. The falling sand test measures the number of litres of sand required to wear a patch of specified diameter. This test is useful for evaluating surface abrasion in countries subject to sand storms.

Gloss reduction.   The normal method of evaluation is to use a 60°

glossmeter to ASTM D523. Readings can be obtained for the original material and for weathered samples or buildings in use.

Formability test. There are various tests available but the conical mandrel test to ASTM D522 gives formability on a bend of varying diameter. The sample must be formed at a constant speed in a given timescale. The coating can then be examined under magnification to identify stretching of the coating, and microcracking to the coating or substrate.

Hardness test. There are again various tests available to BS 3900 and ASTM 3363. The pencil hardness test is the easiest to carry out but results vary depending on the skill of the operator. The pencil test measures the hardness of lead required to scratch the coating. With 'leathergrain' Plastisol this is a difficult test to carry out satisfactorily.

Shock impact test. A falling weight indentor is used to form a convex dent in the material which can then be examined under magnification to determine the damage to the coating and the substrate. BS 3900 defines the test requirement.

Adhesion test. A standard cross cut tool is used to score the coating down to the base metal and the degree of flaking measured as a percentage of the cross hatched area. The method is defined in BS 3900.

5.4.2 Accelerated testing

Salt spray. Samples are mounted in the cabinet with top and edge protection. A cross cut is made on the sample and the test run for 1000 hours in accordance with ASTM B117 or other appropriate Standard. The samples are evaluated for defects on completion and at stages during the test. Pre-formed samples must be used for realistic results.

Humidity resistance. The tests to ASTM D2247 and BS 3900 vary and can produce different results. The test to BS 3900 requires the temperature to be cycled hourly between 42°C and 48°C in the presence of free water thus ensuring that condensation occurs. The samples are again cross hatched and the test is run for 1000 hours. The samples are evaluated at 1000 hours and at stages during the test. The ASTM test does not ensure that condensation occurs. Material shipped to the Middle East or Far East in sealed packs will undergo cycling similar to that produced by the BS test for humidity. One cladding material which complied to the ASTM tests suffered repeated failures in the Middle East due to this problem. The same material used on buildings in the UK performed satisfactorily.

Sulphur dioxide test.   This test to BS 3900 provides for an 8 hour period of high humidity and temperature followed by 18 hours at ambient laboratory conditions. At the start of the cycle a measured shot of 2 litres of SO_2 is introduced into the chamber and the temperature is retained at 40°C. There are arguments that the test is too severe, but it does identify any susceptibility of the coating to attack by sulphur dioxide.

Colour fade test.   There are various tests available to predict colour performance. The QUV weatherometer can produce good correlation with colour fade particularly with Plastisol samples and the EMMAQUA can give good comparative results. This latter test uses a natural test site in Arizona but maximises exposure to UV light by focusing sunlight onto the samples using mirrors.

Natural weathering.   In these tests, samples are exposed on test sites at selected locations in rural, industrial or marine environments and evaluated regularly. Often samples are mounted at 45° and orientated to face south. Some exposure tests included a vertical north facing sample. A popular test site was the Nuclear Power Station at Dungeness. This site had a particularly harsh environment and produced rapid degradation to most products produced during the 1970's.

Natural weathering tests are used to evaluate overall performance of materials and in addition to the considerations already discussed under Physical and Accelerated Tests, need to assess dirt retention, mould growth and other factors. Differential colour fade can only be identified if a number of samples from the same colour batch have been exposed.

The South Florida exposure test is accepted as an industry standard and here samples are exposed naturally in the high UV location. Exposure periods vary from 1 to 5 years. This test should be considered as an evaluation of susceptibility to colour change or degradation due to UV light. The UK climate requires other factors to be considered and long term exposure tests in the UK are also necessary.

A problem with natural exposure tests is the time taken to achieve results. In the sphere of product development, this timeframe is unacceptable. The best tests for natural weathering are completed projects! Generally, once completed, projects are not subject to evaluations for cladding performance and only those projects where problems have been identified will be subject to detailed inspection.

5.5 Maintenance

The exterior of a building, like the interior, must be maintained and regular inspection will identify areas for possible attention. In areas of relatively high industrial pollution, washing down of the coating with high pressure jets can prevent the onset of corrosion.

Loose fixings may lead to the ingress of water and corrosion around the fastener. If the lapped roof joints become loose, corrosion may occur to the underside of the sheet at the lapped joint leading ultimately to serious corrosion. If water is allowed to enter via the fasteners, the installation may become damp leading to further corrosion of the underside.

Blocked gutters can lead to the ingress of water to the building or the build up of water onto the building roof. If leaves, dirt and other contaminants are allowed to build up at flashed joints between roof and walls, corrosion can again occur.

Damaged coatings can be touched up and failing coatings overcoated with relative ease provided the problems are identified at an early enough stage. Regular inspection of the cladding to a predetermined schedule can pay dividends in preventing major remedial works. Repair methods are described in Chapter 6.

5.6 Analysis of results of building cladding failures

Large quantities of data on cladding problems and failures have been collected during the preparation of this report and the results are presented in this Chapter. The information has been collected from a variety of sources including responses to questionnaires issued to trade associations, manufacturers, building owners, architects, contractors and surveyors, discussions with these groups, analysis of previously collated data and other sources.

Figures 5.1 to 5.15 at the end of this Chapter present the data collected in graphic form. The problems have been divided into a number of categories. These are listed below with photograph numbers relating to photographs, also at the end of the Chapter, showing some typical defects.

Gloss change	(Photograph 2)
Colour change	(Photographs 2 and 3)
Crazing/flaking	(Photograph 3)
Delamination	(Photographs 4 and 5)
Corrosion at cut edge	(Photographs 6 and 7)

Corrosion of base metal or random corrosion	(Photographs 8 and 9)
Back peel	—
Corrosion around fixings	(Photograph 11)
Rooflights	(Photographs 12 and 13)
Filliform corrosion	(Photograph 14)

Whilst these categories are largely self explanatory some are explained further. Corrosion of base metal refers to the core metal substrate and not to the galvanise coating. Back peel refers to peeling of a coating on the inner surface of the cladding sheet. Rooflights is a general term describing any problem associated with the presence of a rooflight in the construction.

The most widely used coating for industrial buildings over the past 20 years in the UK has been Plastisol and hence there are far more data available for this coating than for other coating types. It is interesting to note that PVDF has been extensively used for industrial purposes in various parts of Europe. Product formulations have changed over the years and in the case of Plastisol the third generation products (Type 3) have a greatly enhanced performance compared with material of the same generic type produced 10 years ago.

Information has been obtained on nearly 500 reported failures of Type 1 (first generation) Plastisol and the various types of failure by cause are shown in Figure 5.1. The remedial action carried out is shown in Figure 5.2 and Table 5.8. The results show that delamination was the major cause of failure with this formulation requiring stripping back of the delaminated area and overpainting. Figure 5.3 shows that more failures were recorded on walls than roofs. This can be explained by two factors: asbestos cement was still widely used at that time for roofs (and hence little coated metal was used for roofs), and roofs are not subject to such regular visual inspection. Figure 5.4 gives the average number of years to failure, gloss change occurring quite quickly but delamination occurring at a later stage. It should be noted that after a period of 10 – 15 years an accurate time history of failures becomes more difficult as owners lose track of material sources and coating types. As a consequence, suppliers tend not to hear about late-life failures.

For Types 2 and 3 Plastisol (second and third generation products) information has been obtained on approximately 200 failures. Figure 5.5 shows the various causes of failure and corrosion at the cut edge has become the most common complaint. Figure 5.6 and Table 5.9 show the remedial action taken. Interestingly, most failures were reported on roofs for Type 2 and 3 Plastisol as shown in Figure 5.7, indicating the increasing use of coated metal cladding and the change away from the use of asbestos cement. Given that the results apply to a similar usage for walls, it is reasonable to assume that the Types 2 and 3 give a far lower incidence of failure. Figure 5.8 gives the distribution of average number of years to failure and, again, the time period represents only the period when failures were reported to the original supplier.

A combination of the results for all versions of Plastisol gives an overall perspective of the various forms of failure as shown in Figure 5.9. The Figures 5.10, 5.11 and 5.12 show the remedial work carried out as tabulated in Table 5.10, the distribution between roof and wall failures and the average number of years to failure for each defect. The figures represent about 0.2% of production of one particular supplier at the upper end of the quality spectrum, hence the average UK statistics will be worse than this. Also, since many failures go unreported, the total figure for this supplier will be higher than the 0.2% indicated.

Some sources of information gave less detail than described above, but an evaluation of over 1700 instances of failure on Plastisol coated sheet demonstrated that nearly 50% of incidences related to corrosion at the cut edge as shown in Figure 5.13. It is not known what percentage of production this represents for the manufacturers concerned.

Data collected for PVDF (PVF2) are more limited, partly due to the smaller quantity of the material used and partly due to the availability of data sources. Figure 5.14 shows the results of 80 recorded failures and demonstrates that corrosion of the cut edge was the most common cause of failure. Corrosion of the base metal is more prevalent with this generic coating type since microcracking of the coating at the bends (often coupled with a similar defect in the galvanising) can result in corrosion of the base metal. Blistering of the coating can also occur leading to ingress of moisture and ultimately corrosion of the base metal. Results of a larger survey of 140 failures are shown in Figure 5.15. Here corrosion of the cut edge again represents the major cause of failure. Due to the varying sources of data, it is not possible to give a detailed breakdown of all the other causes of failure.

5.7 Analysis of test data

Various test programmes on samples of organically coated cladding have been carried out by both manufactures and independent sources. As participators the authors have access to the results of some of these tests. Many tests were carried out on samples of flat material, and the accelerated and natural exposure test results will be valid for gloss and colour performance but not for other material performance characteristics as defects often occur at the formed bend. Other tests have been performed on brake pressed samples where profiled sections have been created artificially by brake pressing the material to form the required shape. Roll formed samples represent the only true calibration with the 'real' situation, but it should be appreciated that different profiles have different bend radii. Base metal thickness may also influence the roll forming process.

One test programme investigated the samples shown in Table 5.1. The Plastisol samples represent Types 1 and 2. In this programme, samples were cut from the original profiled sheets supplied for test. Samples were mounted on test rigs for natural exposure testing, used for accelerated tests, used for physical tests and maintained as reference samples. This programme was believed to be the first using roll formed samples and tracking physical accelerated and site exposure tests for a wide range of samples of different generic type.

The results of the programme are as shown. The physical tests confirmed that Plastisol gave the overall best performance for surface condition tests as shown in Table 5.2. The results of the accelerated tests given in Table 5.3 confirm that cut edge corrosion could be anticipated from most coatings and that Plastisol would be expected to give best results against cut edge corrosion. Examples of the results of some of the tests are shown in Photographs 16 and 17 representing Plastisol and PVDF respectively.

Exposure panels were mounted in a coastal environment, and an industrial environment in the West Midlands. The results were quite similar and the summary for the West Midlands site is quoted in this report in Table 5.4. Ironically, the degree of identified pollution has subsequently declined at both locations. The test rigs exposed the samples, cut from roll formed sheets, on a south-facing elevation with the samples mounted at 45°.

Research into the relationship between the cladding design and environmental factors has been studied in a report commissioned by the EEC. The materials tested included hot dip galvanised, and aluminium/zinc rich coatings and these products are not part of this study. The report included results for polyester and silicone modified polyesters, PVDF and acrylics all on pre-treated steel and some results related to real life performance on buildings.

Results for the inspection of the buildings are summarised in Table 5.5 and indicate that problems with the thin coatings started to occur quite rapidly after erection of the buildings. It should, however, be recognised that all of the claddings were 1960's and 1970's production and improvements have since taken place.

The programme also carried out a series of exposure tests using formed panels. (The panels were formed using a manual fly press which will not fully simulate the conditions of a roll formed sample). The tests included an overlap area, an area of standard damage using a scribed cross, an area of deformation using an indentor and two types of fastener. Various tests were performed including the forming of box structures to assess the effect on different elevations. Results for the exposure tests are shown in Tables 5.6 and 5.7 for a rural and marine site. Other tests were carried out on sample panels exposed in rural, marine, industrial and high UV locations.

The results of the various tests and inspections confirms certain key factors:

¤ The behaviour of formed samples can differ greatly from flat sheet. The profiling process is an important stage in the performance of products.

¤ Natural weathering tests on FORMED samples are the best indicator of product performance but take time before useful results are obtained. Samples should be tested in realistic situations (e.g. vertical faces at various orientations) to simulate product performance.

¤ Accelerated tests can be used to assess corrosion based defects but are less reliable for gloss loss, colour change, chalking and loss of flexibility.

¤ Physical tests give useful data on the characteristics of the coating and can be used for assessing susceptibility to certain problems.

¤ Natural weathering leads to chemical changes in the coatings which can lead to failure.

¤ Thick coatings are more tolerant to abuse during manufacture, site storage, installation and use but are more susceptible to colour fade.

Generic coating type	Substrate	No. of samples	No. of different colours
Plastisol	Galvanised steel	45	17
PVF2A/PVDF	Aluminium/Galvanised steel	23	14
Silicon Modified Polyester	Galvanised steel	5	3
Modified Aklyd	Galvanised steel	1	1
Alkyd Amino	Aluminium	9	7
Acrylic	Galvanised steel	2	2
PVC film	Galvanised steel	2	2
Acrylic film	Galvanised steel	4	4

Table 5.1. Summary of samples tested

Material	Adhesion	Formability	Abrasion (Litres of sand)	Hardness	Impact	Notes
Plastisol (200 micron)	5	Yes	250–560	5H (marks only)	4–5	No pencil cuts surface
PVDF	5	Variable	40	2H–5H	1–3	Micro-cracking on some samples for formability assessment
PVF2A +	5	Yes	35	2H–5H	3–4	
SMP	5	No	20	4H–5H	1	Cracking of coating on formability assessment
Modified Alkyd	5	No	10	5H (marks only)	1	Cracking of coating on formability assessment
Alkyd Amino +	5	No	7	3H	4	Coating cracks on forming but is applied after roll forming
Acrylic	5	Yes	45	2H	2	
PVC film	5	Yes	570	5H	4–5	5H pencil just scratches surface
Acrylic film	5	Yes	80	2H	4	

5 = Good performance; 0 = Serious failure; + = Aluminium substrate

Table 5.2 Summary of physical tests

Material	Salt spray			Humidity			Artificial weathering			Sulphur dioxide			Comments
	Flats	Ridges	Edge	Flats	Ridges	Edge	Flats	Ridges	Edge	Flats	Ridges	Edge	Aluminium Substrate
Plastisol (200 micron)	5	5	2–5	5	5	4	5	5	5	5	5	3–5	Little colour change. Some gloss loss on humidity and sulphur dioxide tests
PVDF	3–5	2–1	2–5	5	5	4	5	5	5	2–5	1–5	2–3	Colour change on sulphur dioxide test. Some gloss loss on sulphur dioxide and artificial weathering tests
PVF2A+	5	5	5	3–5	5	5	5	5	5	2	2	4–5	Colour and gloss loss on sulphur dioxide test
SMP	2	2	0–5	1–4	1–2	4	5	3	4	1–2	1–2	2–5	Colour change on sulphur dioxide test. Gloss loss on humidity and sulphur dioxide tests
Modified Alkyd	5	1	1–3	5	5	5	5	2	5	5	0	3	Some colour change on salt spray and sulphur dioxide tests. Little gloss loss
Alkyd Amino +	5	4	5	5	5	5	5	5	5	0–2	0–2	0–2	Little colour change. Gloss loss on sulphur dioxide test
Acrylic	5	1	2	3	1	4	5	5	5	1	1	2	Colour change on sulphur dioxide test. Some gloss loss on all except salt spray test
PVC film	5	5	1–5	5	5	5	5	5	5	5	5	3–5	Little colour change or gloss loss
Acrylic film	5	3	1–5	4	5	4	5	5	5	3	3	3	Colour change on humidity and sulphur dioxide test. Gloss loss on sulphur dioxide tests

5 = Good performance; 0 = Serious failure; SMP = Silicone modified polyester

Table 5.3. Summary of accelerated test results

Coating type	Dirt retention	Colour change	Gloss change	Undercoating	Notes
Plastisol (200 micron)	2–3	3½–4 (3 on two samples)	Severe loss	Small 0–3 mm	No cracking or blistering Severe fade on 04B29, O8C3S and fade on 10B19 Colour change to O8B29 and 12B29, some bleaching of plasticiser
PVDF	2–3	4–5	Some loss	Small 0–3 mm	Colour retention good Microcracking and slight blistering generally evident
PVF 2A	2–3	–4–4½	Some loss	None	Slight darkening to some samples, but good colour retention Slight microcracking and blistering evident
SMP	3	4	Some loss	Up to 2 mm	Marked cracking and blistering at bends Rust staining on bends Some chalking
Modified Alkyd	2	4½	Severe loss	None	Severe chalking Marked cracking at bends with rust staining
Alkyd Amino	2–3	–4–4	Some loss	None	Some blistering to the coating Medium chalking Colour retention generally good
Acrylic	2–3	4–5	Some loss	1 mm	Microcracking and blistering to coating Good colour retention
PVC film	2–3	4–5	Some loss	2 mm	No cracking or blistering Good overall appearance and colour
Acrylic film	2	4–5	Some loss	Up to 2 mm	Slight blistering but no microcracking Good colour retention

5 = Good performance; 0 = Serious failure

Table 5.4. Summary of exposure panels results — West Midlands rig

Location/ type	Year constructed	Age in years at inspection	Environment	Coating type/colour	Profile bend radius mm	Orientation of slide	Comments
Milton Keynes office warehouse	1979	1	Urban/rural	PVDF/White	4·5	All sides	Slight cracking at corner bends, radius 2·75 mm
Leicester/office factory etc.	1976	4	Rural	PVDF/Cream brown	4	Most sides	Medium cracking, slight blistering on profile peak bends. Cracks were on the building corners and cill bends. Heavy white corrosion products at cut edges in a sheltered region
Milton Keynes office warehouse	1976	4	Urban/rural	PVDF/White	4·5	All sides	Slight cracking and blistering on peak bends, moderate cracking on corner bends, radium 3 mm
Leicester power station	1973–74	6	Industrial/ urban	PVDF/Dark brown	4·5	All sides	Slight blistering on profile peaks, generally, but moderate blistering on profile peaks near to source of pollution. Slight cracking and blistering on peak bends, slight blistering on vertical edges
Holyhead conveyor	1970	10	Severe marine	PVDF/Grey	4·5	South west	Isolated and rust spots on profile peaks and bends. Moderate blistering on bends. Heavy red rusting with heavy blistering up to 50 mm from horizontal cut edges. Moderate blistering up to 10 mm from vertical cut edges. Lines of heavy red rust staining on cladding from around fastener, slight blistering immediately adjacent to fasteners
						North east	As south west side but severe corrosion of the steel substrate with associated creep back and flaking on some parts of the horizontal edges and on the underpart of a door frame
Factory	1968	12	Urban	PVDF/Blue	6	East and south	Moderate chalking with associated heavy loss of gloss and some colour fade on profile peaks. Slight cracking and slight blistering on peak bends. Slight blistering on profile troughs

Table 5.5. Results of building inspections

Location/type	Year constructed	Age in years at inspection	Environment	Coating type/colour	Profile bend radius mm	Orientation of slide	Comments
Belgium/industrial works	1971	9	Industrial	Silicone Acrylic/Dark blue	4·5	South	Heavy chalking and associated colour fade, slight to moderate cracking on peak bends. Slight white corrosion products at cut edges
West Germany/factory	1970	11	Urban/light industrial	Polyester/Blue	4·75/5·5	All sides	As west, slight to moderate blistering and some cracks at peak bends. Also continuous red rusting of bends on some localised areas on east face and west facing bends close to north west corner on north face. On occasional bends, heavy flaking with heavy red rusting. On the east face, red rusting and associated creep back (2 mm) present on bottom horizontal edge
West Germany/factory	1970	11	Urban/light industrial	Polyester/Blue	4·75/5·5	All sides	Slight chalking, moderate to heavy loss of gloss, some colour fade. All peak bends visibly cracked and associated with slight red and white corrosion products blistering. Very slight blistering on profile peaks and troughs. Occasional fine blisters and slight white rust on horizontal edges and very slight red rust on vertical edges
Belgium/factory	1967/69	13	Urban/industrial	Acrylic/Light blue	4·25/4·5	All sides	Heavy chalking and gloss reduction. All peak bends and cill bends cracked with heavy red rusting at cracks. Red rusting was continuous on all bends on the south and west faces. Slight white corrosion products at horizontal cut edges
West Germany/office	1965	17	Industrial	Acrylic/White	4·75/5·5	South	Heavy chalking and gloss reduction. Slight blistering at peak bends, slight red and white corrosion products with slight blistering (up to 3 mm) at cut edges
						West	As south, but cracks also present on peak bends. Moderate blistering up to 10 mm from horizontal cut edges

Table 5.5. Results of building inspections (continued)

Material	PE//Zn (Grey)				SPE/Zn				SPE/A1-Zn				PVDF/Zn			
Orientation of side	North	East	South	West	North	East	South	West	North	East	South	West	North	East	South	West
Chalking	O	O	O	O	O	O	O	O	O	O	O	O	O	O	O	O
Eaves area General surface	1B	1B	O	1B	O	O	O	O	O	O	O	O	O	O	O	O
Bends: Narrow end Wide end Top edge main panel	1B 1B 2B3	1B 1B 2B3	1B 1B 2B3	1B 1B 2B3	* * 1B1	* * 1B1	* * 1B1	* * 1B1	1B 1B 3B5	1B 1B 3B5	1B 1B 3B5	1B 1B 3B5	3B60 3B60 2B2	1B30 1B30 2B2	3B30 2B30 2B2	3B30 2B30 2B2
General surface	O	O	O	O	O	O	O	O	O	O	O	O	O	O	O	O
90° bends	O	O	O	O	O	O	O	O	O	O	O	O	O	O	O	O
Cut edges main panel Bottom Others	1B1 1B1	1B1 1B1	1B1 1B1	1B1 1B1	1F1 1B1	1F1 1B1	1F1 1B1	1F1 1B1	3B4 3B4	3B4 3B3	3B4 3B3	2B2 3B3	1B1 1B1	1B1 1B1	1B1 1B1	1B1 1B1
Areas of panel adjacent to overlap panel	O	O		O	O	O	O	O	O	O	O	O	O	O	O	O
Overlap panel cut edge Bottom Others	1B1 1B1	1B1 1B1	1B1 1B1	1B1 1B1	1B1 1B1	1B1 1B1	1B1 1B1	1B1 1B1	3B5 3B5	3B4 3B4	3B4 3B4	3B4 3B4	1B1 1B1	1B1 1B1	1B1 1B1	1B1 1B1
Erichsen Dome	O	O	O	O	1F	1F	O	1F	1B 2W	2W	2W	2W	O	O	O	O

B = Blistering; F = Flaking; W = White rusting; * = Cracks in coating opening up; PE = Polyester; SPE = Silicone modified polyester
First number relates to severity of defects which increases with numerical value
Second number relates to extent of defect in mm

Table 5.6. Exposure test results: vertical sides — rural site — three years

Material	PE/Zn (Grey)				SPE/Zn				SPE/A1-Zn				PVDF/Zn			
Orientation of side	North	East	South	West	North	East	South	West	North	East	South	West	North	East	South	West
Chalking	0	0	0	0	1	1	1	1	0	0	0	0	0	0	0	0
Eaves area General surface	3B	1W 1B	1B	1B	0	0	0	0	0	0	0	0	0	0	0	0
Bends: Narrow end	2B	2B	2B	2B	5F55	5F60	5F60	5F60	0	1B	0	0	4B	4B	4B	4B
Wide end	2B	2B	2B	2B	2F50	2F50	5F30	5F30	0	0	0	0	4B	4B	4B	4B
Top edge main panel	3W 3B2	3W 2B5	3W 2B5	3W 2B5	3B3	3B5	3B5	3B5	2W	3B4	2B4	2B4	3B5	3B3	3B3	3B3
General surface	0	0	0	0	0	0	0	0	0	0	0	0	0	0	0	0
90° bends	1B	1B	1B	1B	5F *	5F *	0	0	0	0	0	0	4B	4B	4B	4B
Cut edges main panel Bottom	2W 3B3	2W 2B2	2W 2B2	2W 2B2	3B2 3F2	2B5 3F3	2B5 3F3	2B5 3F3	2B2	2B2	2B4	2B4	3B2	3B4 2F4	3B4	3B4
Others	2W 3B3	2W 2B2	2W 2B2	2W 2B2	3B2	2B2 3F2	2B2 3F2	2B2 3F2	3B5	3B5	2B4	2B4	2B2	3B4 2F4	3B4	3B4
Areas of panel Adjacent to overlap panel	0	0	0	0	0	0	0	0	0	0	0	0	0	0	0	0
Overlap panel cut Bottom	2W ??	2W 2B3	2W 2B3	2W 2B3	5F3	5F2	5F2	5F2	3B5	3B5	2B4	3B4	2B2	2B1	2B1	2B1
Others	2W ??	2W	2W	2W	5F3	5F2	5F2	5F2	3B4	3B4	2B4	3B4	2B2	2B1 3F1	2B1 2F1	2B1
Erichsen Dome	0	0	0	0	1F	1F	1F	1F	2W	2W	1W	1W	4B	4B	4B	4B

F = Flaking; W = White rusting; R = Red rusting; RS = Rust staining; WP = White rust pustules; NA = Not applicable; * = Bottom of bends only
PE = Polyester; SPE = Silicone modified polyester
First number relates to severity of defects which increases with numerical value
Second number relates to extent of defect in mm

Table 5.7. Exposure test results: vertical sides — marine site — three years

Problem type	Total no.	Remedial work undertaken				
		Paint edges	None	Strip and refix	Overpaint	Overclad
Gloss change	12	0	3	0	9	0
Colour change	103	0	13	2	88	0
Crazing/flaking	6	0	0	0	6	0
Delamination	340	2	50	18	267	3
Corrosion at cut edge	21	7	6	0	8	0
Corrosion of base metal	10	0	6	1	3	0
Back peel	0					
Corrosion around fixings	0					
Rooflights	0					
Filliform corrosion	0					
	492	9	78	21	381	3

Table 5.8. Distribution of remedial work — Plastisol type 1

Problem type	Total no.	Paint edges	Remedial work undertaken			
			None	Strip and refix	Overpaint	Overclad
Gloss change	1	0	0	1	0	0
Colour change	29	0	18	3	8	0
Crazing/flaking	1	0	0	0	1	0
Delamination	46	0	14	14	18	0
Corrosion at cut edge	103	96	5	2	0	0
Corrosion of base metal	8	0	8	0	0	0
Back peel	4	0	4	0	0	0
Corrosion around fixings	0					
Rooflights	0					
Filliform corrosion	0					
	192	96	49	20	27	0

Table 5.9. Distribution of remedial work — Plastisol types 2 and 3

Problem type	Total no.	Remedial work undertaken						
		Paint edges	None	Strip and refix	Overpaint	Overclad	Not known
Gloss change	13	0	3	1	9	0	0
Colour change	135	0	31	5	93	0	3
Crazing/flaking	8	0	0	0	7	0	1
Delamination	403	2	64	32	285	3	17
Corrosion at cut edge	140	103	11	2	8	0	16
Corrosion of base metal	18	0	14	1	3	0	0
Back peel	4	0	4	0	0	0	0
Corrosion around fixings	2	0	0	0	0	0	2
Rooflights	1	0	0	0	0	0	1
Filliform corrosion	0						
	724	105	127	41	405	3	40

Table 5.10. Distribution of remedial work — all types

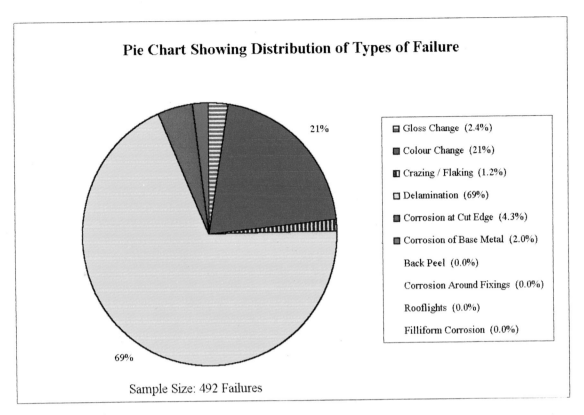

Fig. 5.1. Plastisol type 1

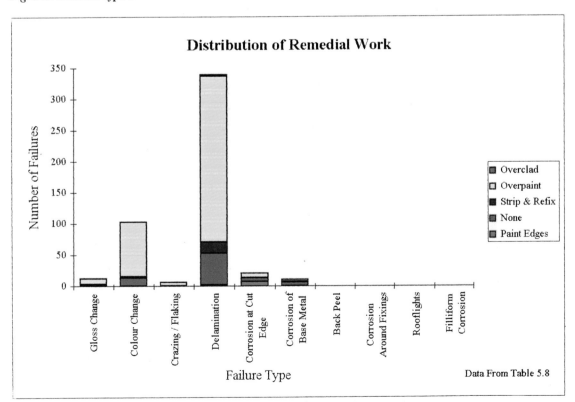

Fig. 5.2. Plastisol type 1

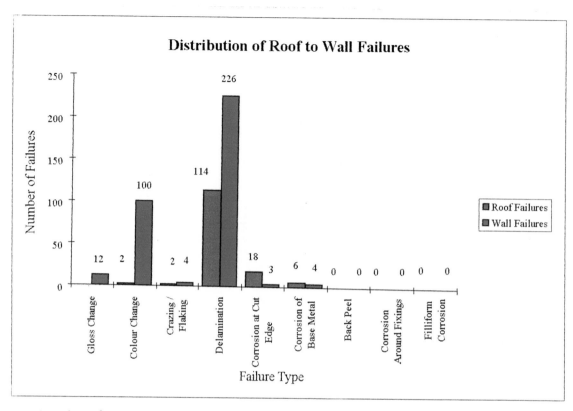

Fig. 5.3. Plastisol type 1

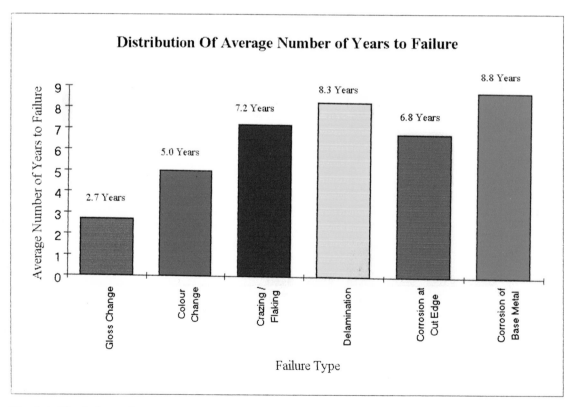

Fig. 5.4. Plastisol type 1

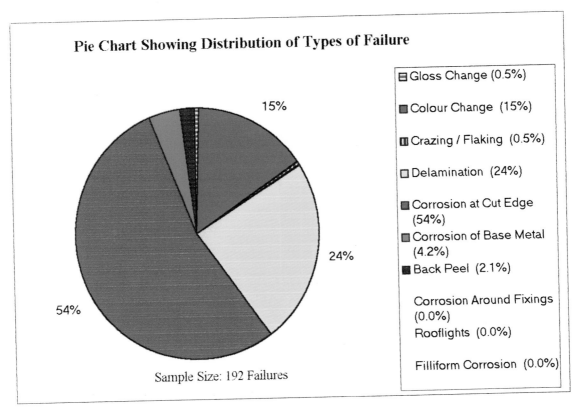

Fig. 5.5. Plastisol types 2 and 3

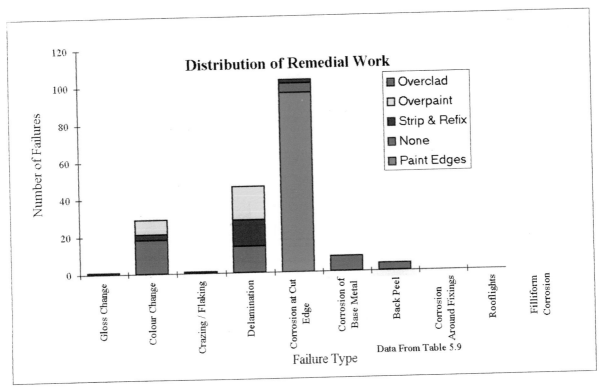

Fig. 5.6. Plastisol types 2 and 3

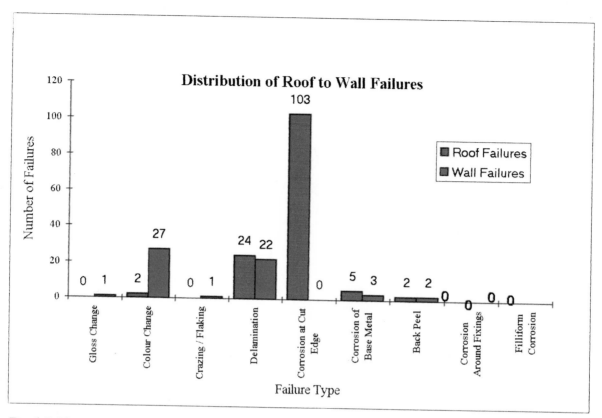

Fig. 5.7. Plastisol types 2 and 3

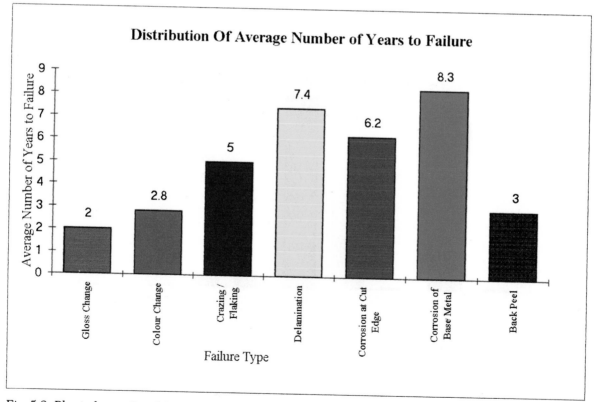

Fig. 5.8. Plastisol types 2 and 3

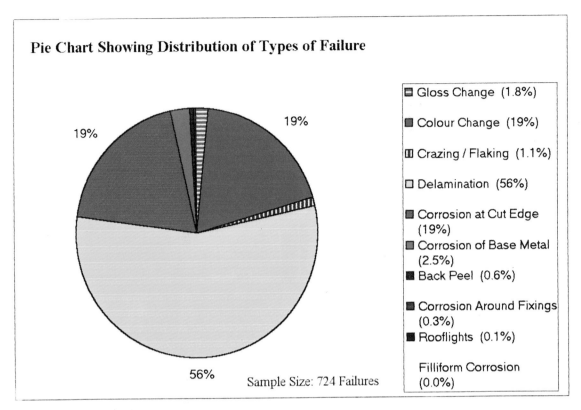

Fig. 5.9. *Plastisol – all types*

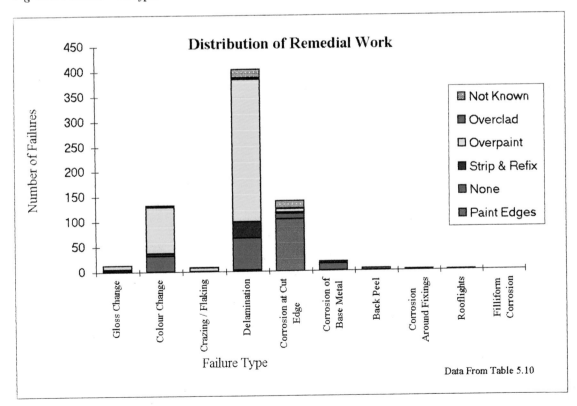

Fig. 5.10. *Plastisol – all types*

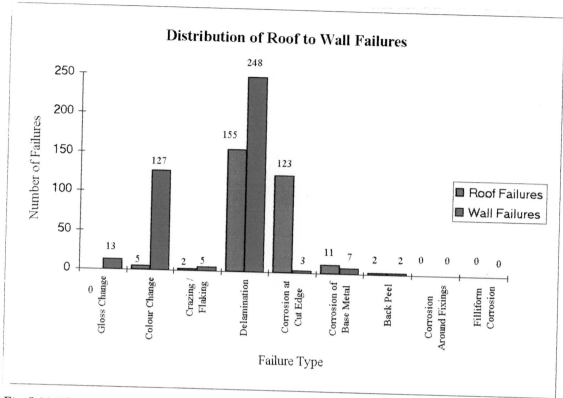

Fig. 5.11. Plastisol – all types

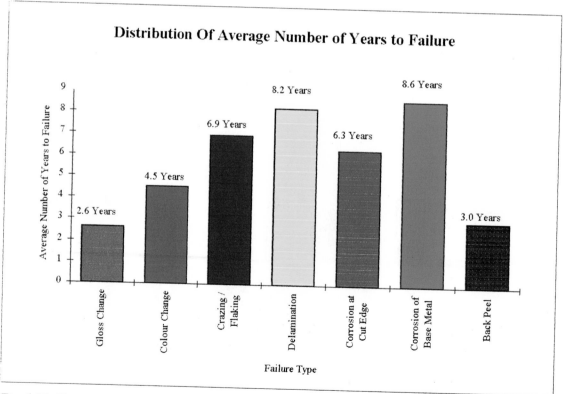

Fig. 5.12. Plastisol – all types

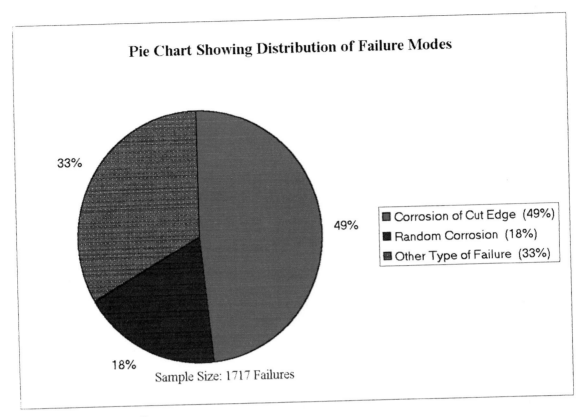

Fig. 5.13. *Plastisol – all types*

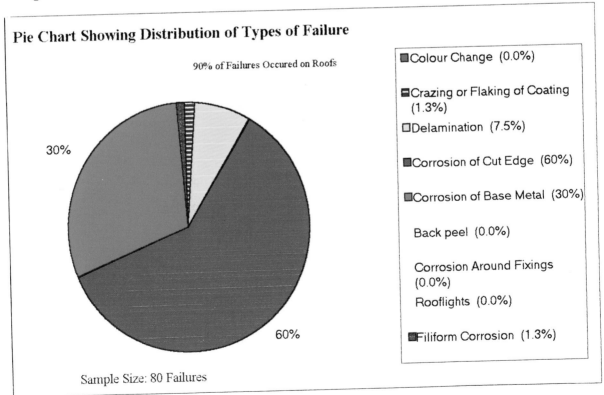

Fig. 5.14. *PVDF*

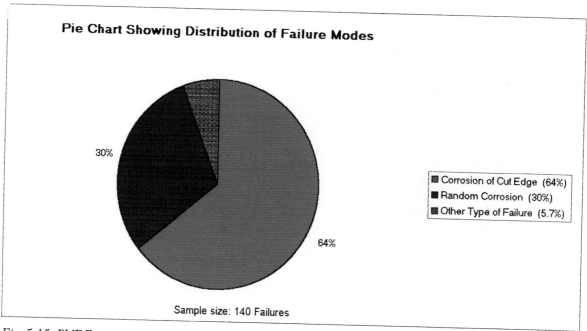

Fig. 5.15. PVDF

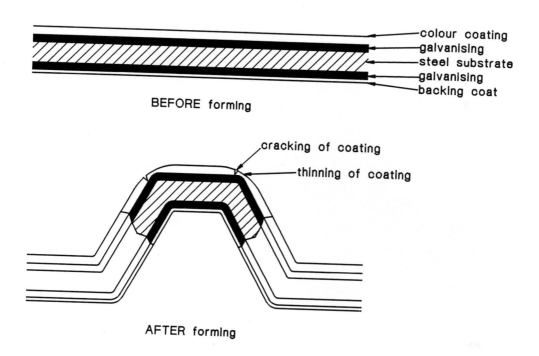

Fig. 5.16. Sheet deformation problems

Photo 1. The roll forming process

Photo 2. Defect: gloss change/colour variation

Photo 3. Defect: colour change and flaking

Photo 4. Defect: delamination

Photo 5. Defect: delamination

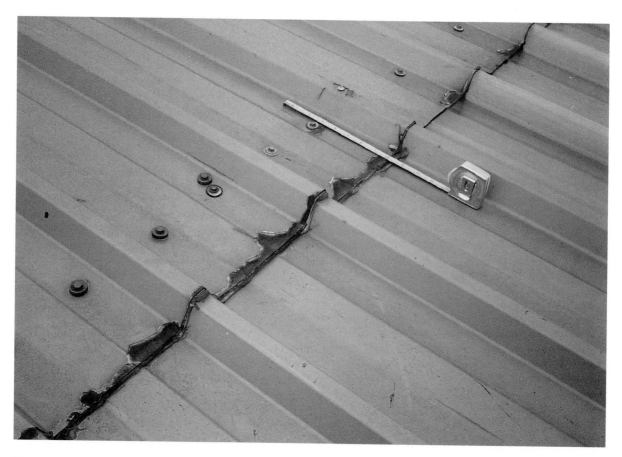

Photo 6. Defect: cut edge corrosion

Photo 7. Defect: cut edge corrosion/poor maintenance

Photo 8. Defect: corrosion of base metal

Photo 9. Defect: corrosion of base metal

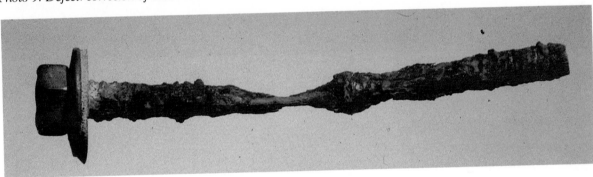

Photo 10. Defect: fixing – corrosion at damp interface between layers (waisted section)

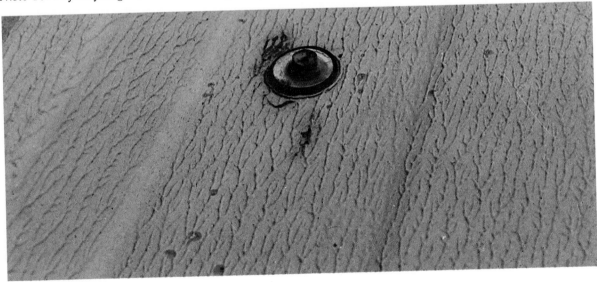

Photo 11. Defect: fixing – corrosion of head due to missing cap and corrosion of sheet due to drilling swarf

Photo 12. Defect: rooflight – incorrect fixing

Photo 13. Defect: rooflight – distortion due to inadequate thickness

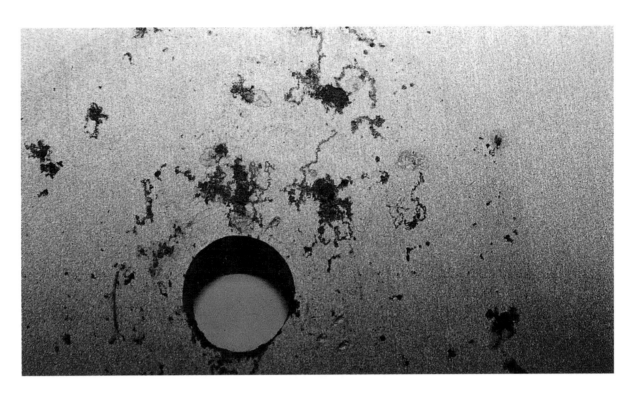

Photo 14. Defect: filiform corrosion

Photo 15. Defect: workmanship – inadequate end lap, no sealant

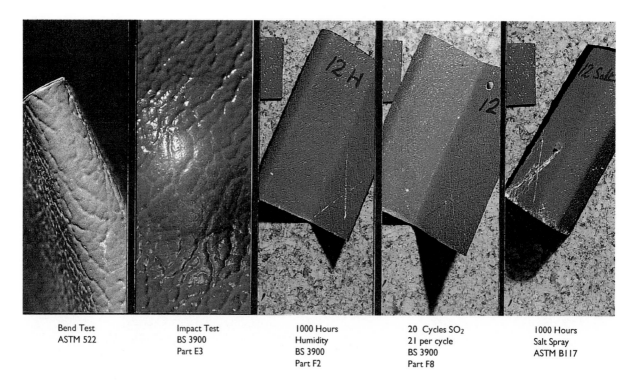

Bend Test ASTM 522	Impact Test BS 3900 Part E3	1000 Hours Humidity BS 3900 Part F2	20 Cycles SO₂ 21 per cycle BS 3900 Part F8	1000 Hours Salt Spray ASTM B117

Photo 16. Accelerated test specimens – Plastisol

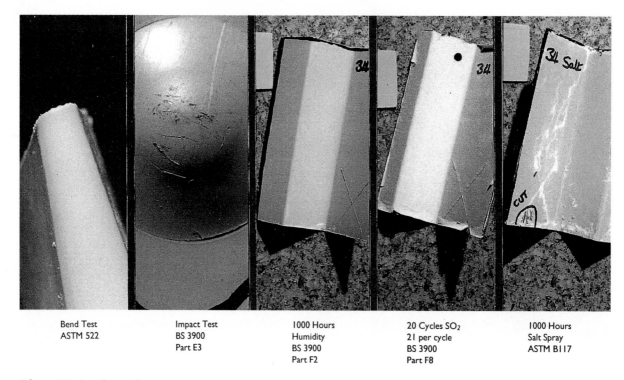

Bend Test ASTM 522	Impact Test BS 3900 Part E3	1000 Hours Humidity BS 3900 Part F2	20 Cycles SO₂ 21 per cycle BS 3900 Part F8	1000 Hours Salt Spray ASTM B117

Photo 17. Accelerated test specimens – PVDF

6. Repair methods

6.1 Preliminary

The performance of any cladding material depends on a number of factors from cladding manufacture through to regular maintenance of the building facade. However, even well maintained organically coated sheet will eventually start to deteriorate.

Reasons for poor performance can include damage on site, inadequate design, incorrect or poorly fixed fasteners or corrosion. Premature failure due to inadequate coating formulation or application can occur but this is small in comparison to production when the material has been produced under controlled quality assured processing conditions.

Whatever the reason for failure, the useful life of the cladding can be extended by repainting affected areas or, where necessary, overpainting. In this report repainting is defined as removal of the original coating and application of new paint, whilst overpainting is defined as the application of paint directly onto the original coating.

Pre-painted sheet cladding is produced using sophisticated manufacturing processes in controlled factory conditions. The paint is applied to consistent thickness and cured or dried by stoving. In contrast, site applied paints have to contend with a wide variety of environmental conditions and are air drying.

The factors to be taken into account when considering paint repairs are discussed in this Chapter.

6.2 Degradation process

The sequence of deterioration is generally categorised into four phases, although these do not necessarily happen sequentially in every case.

6.2.1. Chalking, loss of gloss or colour change

A gradual change in appearance occurs as the sheet weathers, this does not affect the functional performance of the roof or cladding and will not normally be a cause for painting. However, overpainting can be a requirement where appearance is important.

6.2.2. Crazing or flaking

In this phase the coating begins to fail. A very fine crazing of the coating, known as micro-checking, occurs over progressively larger areas. Where crazing penetrates the coating down to the galvanise or metal substrate, the corrosion process starts and flaking of the coating can occur.

It is at this stage that overpainting should be carried out to prevent further deterioration and maintain the integrity of the cladding.

6.2.3. Corrosion of galvanising (steel cladding)

If crazing or flaking is left untreated, any zinc or aluminium-zinc galvanise coating will start to corrode. Typically, patches of white rust appear, peel back of the coating becomes more extensive and corrosion of the base metal becomes apparent.

It is still possible at this stage to maintain the integrity of the cladding. Repainting rather than overpainting will be necessary. The original coating must be stripped from affected areas and the inorganic corrosion protection system treated before repainting affected areas.

6.2.4. Base metal corrosion

During this phase the corrosion process continues unchecked until the cladding perforates. The only course of action then would be to replace the cladding. Over-cladding can be considered, but careful attention will be required with regard to the structural capacity of the roof and potential problems with interstitial condensation.

6.3 Paint selection

Any paint system must have:

- ¤ Compatibility with the original coating
- ¤ Good inter-layer adhesion
- ¤ Resistance to water, chemicals and mould growth
- ¤ Capability to flex with the substrate
- ¤ Good colour retention and ultra-violet resistance

¤   Impact resistance and film hardness.

Additionally, the paint must be capable of application by brush or spray over a wide range of environmental conditions. The paint contractor will have to contend with mist, rain, wind and extremes of temperature and any paint that is not tolerant of surface moisture or normal ambient temperatures will restrict the application window within the working day with consequent financial penalty.

Clearly, a high performance paint system is required, one which is specially formulated for the purpose, and it is recommended that the reader seeks the advice of paint manufacturers with experience and capability in this field.

Advances in paint technology have led to the development of single pack urethane primers and topcoats which are moisture tolerant. Two pack urethanes for which the rate of cure is dependent on ambient temperature and which are sensitive to moisture were followed by moisture cured single pack urethane paints. However, care is required with the application of these paints since they can cure too quickly in the presence of excess moisture. A surface skin is formed leaving the main body of the paint in contact with the substrate uncured and entrapping carbon dioxide produced by the cure reaction.

Single pack urethanes are now available where moisture only triggers the cure reaction of latent hardeners in the paint and produces no carbon dioxide. Paint manufacturers claim that excess moisture is not a problem since the paints can cure underwater with little loss of their mechanical properties.

A further advantage of single pack systems is that they can be subsequently overpainted without the need for an undercoat or primer.

6.4 Inspection

Any roof or cladding which is to be painted should be brought to a good state of repair before repainting. A detailed and comprehensive inspection of the original cladding must therefore be made and remedial works carried out before repainting.

Where the cladding material cannot be identified from drawings or original invoices, samples should be taken and sent for laboratory analysis since, without proper knowledge of the existing coatings, the correct paint cannot be specified.

Often repaint specifications only address the visible surfaces. However, premature failure of the cladding due to back peel may result if unseen sources of corrosion are left untreated.

The inspection should identify:

¤ The substrate, inorganic coating (e.g. galvanising), organic coating and their general condition.

¤ The type, condition and tightness of fixings. The latter can be achieved by hand tightening using a spanner or torque-wrench.

¤ The type and condition of side and end lap seals.

¤ Any corrosion to the underside of cladding, particularly at end laps, side laps and gutter overhangs.

¤ Any damaged sheeting, trims, rooflights, pipe flashings, ventilators or other physical defect.

¤ The nature and source of any environmental pollution or local pollution, e.g. extract ducts.

6.5 Cleaning

A specification for cleaning should be prepared which will vary dependent on the site environment, type of original coating and the degree and type of pollutant or dirt. Where possible the advice of the cladding supplier should be sought.

The cladding should be cleaned using a mild detergent, normally a 2% – 5% detergent to 98% – 95% water mixture. The whole area should be scrubbed to remove dirt, taking care not to damage coatings. Surfaces should then be washed with clean drinking quality water to remove all traces of detergent. Where necessary the process should be repeated to remove all traces of dirt.

The use of solvent or abrasive cleaning agents or strong detergents should be avoided since these may damage the coating. Engrained or heavy accumulations of dirt may be removed using a steam cleaning process but it is recommended that a small trial is carried out first to establish the suitability of the process.

Where microbes, fungus or other living organisms are present, treatment with a fungicide or other eradication measures will be necessary. Dependent on the level of fouling the fungicide should be left on the cladding for up to 7 days. All traces of the fungicide and effluent should be removed and surfaces thoroughly rinsed with drinking quality water.

6.6 Overpainting

6.6.1 Surface preparation

For sound weathered coating the surface should be thoroughly cleaned and any remedial repairs made prior to application of new paint.

Where any individual cladding sheet or flashing has been replaced, but will be overpainted as part of the works, the surface should be degreased. For example, new unweathered PVC coatings should be wiped clean with white spirits, the spirits allowed to evaporate and the surface washed to remove all traces of dirt or other contamination.

6.6.2 Paint application

The prepared surface should then be painted with a single pack moisture tolerant primer and topcoat in accordance with the paint manufacturer's recommendations.

Paint should be applied evenly with particular attention given to achieving a good standard of finish. Work should proceed across the width of sheets such that wet edge areas are maintained when the following strip is painted; double coating should be restricted to 75mm and wherever possible to fixing/purlin lines or sheet ends.

6.7 Re-painting

6.7.1 Removal of original coating

Where the original coating has low adhesion to the substrate, is flaking or peeling, it must be removed using a sharpened paint scraper or hydroblasting technique.

Hydroblasting is a specialist operation and should only be carried out by properly trained personnel. The technique can involve the use of a sand/water slurry; it can also be used in conjunction with a paint stripper. However, the maximum pressure used must be controlled so that no damage occurs to the substrate.

Specialist paint strippers can be used to remove organic coatings. The choice of stripper should be made in conjunction with the supplier and cladding manufacturer. The stripper should be applied evenly in accordance with the manufacturer's recommendations and all traces of chemical and effluent removed by washing using drinking quality water. Care should be taken to ensure that chemical or effluent does not enter gutters or cause damage to surrounding paintwork, roofing etc.

Any visible zinc salts should be removed by washing within the same working day. Where this is not possible light dry abrasion will be necessary.

6.7.2 Surface preparation

In addition to the stripping and cleaning operations described above, all red or white rusted areas should be cleaned to Swedish Standard 2½. Surfaces should be cleaned to standard Sa 2½ in accordance with BS 7079 : Part A1 (ISO 8501-1). Surfaces should be clean, dry and bright but not polished.

When using any paint system the recommendations of the manufacturer should be followed but, in general, preparation of the bare metal substrate will include:

Aluminium	apply a PVB/phenolic chromate primer
Bright Galvanise	apply a mordant wash
Bare Steel	apply anti corrosion primer, a second primer coat should be applied at sheet ends and edges

The experience of some paint suppliers has shown that with some paint systems pretreatment of galvanised surfaces is not always necessary. Moisture cured urethane prepolymer paint systems which require no pre-treatment on galvanised surfaces, and give reliable adhesion, are available.

6.7.3 Paint application

As for overpainting above.

6.8 Chapter references

Some useful references relating to the specification and practical aspects of repair are given below.

References 6, 8, 9, 12, 17, 20

7. Risk of failure

7.1 Preliminary

A prerequisite to any discussion on the risk of failure to coated metal cladding is to define failure. An architect or building owner may consider that a cladding has failed if the colour fades or changes colour, whereas for a building user the criteria might be that there should be no leaks. This Chapter does not seek to define failure but rather discusses a number of factors and the way in which they affect the performance of organically coated metal cladding.

7.2 Solar, temperature and moisture effects

The three major factors which affect performance of organic coatings are ultra-violet radiation, temperature and moisture. The degree of exposure to sun and rain is therefore a key influence, making the orientation or aspect of a building an important consideration. In the UK a south facing elevation or roof will be subject to more ultra-violet light and so coatings will have a shorter life to first maintenance than those on complementary north facing elevations.

Colours will perform differently when exposed to sunlight. White or black are very effective ultra-violet barriers but other pigmentation unable to block the UV will have a shorter life. In general, lighter colours will prove more durable. Additionally, cladding finished in lighter colours reflects heat and does not reach such high temperatures as when dark pigmentation is used, thus providing a better environment for the coating.

Lighter coloured claddings, which reach lower temperatures relative to dark colours due to solar gain, have other advantages in that thermal expansion of the cladding is less and so possible failure of fixings or elongation of fixing holes less likely. It is also worth noting that when the temperature of zinc coated steel cladding rises above 70°C, in the presence of water, which might be trapped between sheets at end laps, reverse galvanic corrosion can occur, that is, the steel corrodes preferentially to the zinc.

All organic coatings are permeable. Thermoplastic material such as PVC is applied in thicknesses up to 200 microns and when saturated the coating itself is prone to deterioration. Thermosetting fluorocarbon type resins on the other hand have very much thinner coatings, usually about 25 microns, which tend to be more permeable making it more likely for substrate corrosion to be the failure mode in the presence of excessive moisture. Roof pitches and building details should be such that rain or snow are removed from the sheeting as quickly as possible.

Soffit areas typically do not get washed down on a regular basis, if at all. Where these areas are regularly subjected to the formation of condensation, which may be contaminated dependent on the building use, the thinner resin coatings do not always perform well.

As exposure to ultra-violet rays, and hence performance, is affected by the building orientation, so is exposure to prevailing weather influences. In the UK, for coatings sensitive to water related degradation problems, orientation of the cladding is important. For example, north facing elements may have a shorter life than others since they will not dry out as quickly as those facing south. Also since the prevailing wind direction in the UK is south-west and hence south-west facing cladding will receive more frequent wetting, these elevations too may have a shorter life than others. More detailed information is needed to determine the effects of orientation on coating durability. Performance will vary with colour and coating and it is not unknown for specifiers to call for different colours for different elevations in order to achieve a uniform life to first maintenance.

Roofs will have a shorter life expectancy than walls for two main reasons. Roofs experience more direct heat of the sun and thus coatings are subject to more rapid degradation due to ultra-violet rays. Also, the rate at which water can be drained off a roof reduces as the pitch decreases. Low pitch roofs will hold water, particularly at end laps in sheeting where capillary forces and driving rain will trap water between sheets. It is for this reason that edge peel is generally associated with roofs. The necessity for roof pitch to not only be compatible with sheeting profile but also to be able to shed water quickly was cited by respondents to our questionnaire as the second most important aspect of design requiring more attention. Rain held at laps encourages corrosion at the exposed edge and delamination of the coating. As curl back of the coating occurs, water accumulates in a small pool behind the upturned coating and dirt collects. A tide mark is often seen where water has been standing. The rate of deterioration of the coating increases if left untreated and can eventually result in edge corrosion and perforation of the base metal.

7.3 Environmental factors

The effect that environmental factors have on the performance of coated metal claddings has already been mentioned. In industrial areas atmospheric pollution can have a detrimental effect. Certainly it is not unknown for badly designed extract flues, which deposit exhaust gases directly onto roofing or cladding, to cause premature local failure of the cladding and general atmospheric pollution will shorten the life of coatings overall, particularly where building details allow dirt and water to collect.

The compatibility of an organic coating with the general environment should be considered, for example Plastisol sheet should not be specified for use on airport buildings since kerosene can cause staining and breakdown of the coating; experience has shown that a PVDF coating is more appropriate for this particular application.

Aggressive environments, including marine, will subject cladding to pollutants, debris or wind blown salt laden spray which will shorten its working life. In these cases it is particularly important to design sheet cladding details to avoid as much site cutting as possible, to avoid details which permit ponding or allow dust and debris to collect where a poultice of contaminants will degrade coatings and to avoid overhangs which are difficult to clean. Buildings located in these difficult environments should receive maintenance on a regular basis, to include washing down and checks on the tightness of fastenings as well as the condition of sealant joints between sheets.

7.4 Site practice

The consequences of edge peel back were described above in Section 7.2. Cut edge corrosion, which often leads on to edge peel back, is the most commonly reported mode of failure and is frequently associated with incorrect site cutting. The use of a hacksaw or an abrasive disc will leave a rough burred edge which will encourage retention of water and lead to failure of the coating. Such cutting methods can also damage the coating because of the heat generated. All site cutting should be kept to a minimum and should be done with a sheet nibbler designed specifically to cut profiled sheeting and flashings. After cutting, all swarf should be removed since it will lead to rust staining, discolouration of the cladding and possibly corrosion. (See Photograph 11.)

Site handling and quality control of cladding materials should ensure no damage since any seemingly minor abrasion or damaged edge can result in early failure of the material. Profiled metal sheeting is delivered to site in a stack, often comprising different length sheets. The sheets are usually banded together with the top and bottom sheets being for packaging only. It is important that proper cranage facilities are available on site to unload sheets in order to avoid damage to sheet edges or local buckling of the profile. Sheets should not be stored uncovered for protracted periods, apart from the obvious potential for accidental damage, any moisture that gets between the sheets cannot dry off and coatings are then at risk of staining or colour change. Sheets should never be slid from the stack as this may scratch the coating; they should be lifted off individually and transported manually to their place of fixing to avoid damage by inappropriate slings or chains.

Site practice was often mentioned by respondents to our questionnaire with regard to risk of failure. A number of respondents commented that available budget and the recession are contributing to future performance problems. Whilst it is true that current pricing practice reflects good value to the client, it is important to ensure that standards of material specification and good site practice are maintained.

Examples were reported of steel sheets with thicknesses normally used on walls that were being used on roofs. Indeed one cladding contractor stated that they had withdrawn from the roofing market because they were not prepared to fix roofs with such sheets.

7.5 Roll forming

The roll forming process which turns flat sheet into profiled metal sheeting is not a theoretical science but rather the product of practical experience. Failures have been recorded where extensive pin-holes have occurred in thin coatings which could not cope with the forming that the sheet was subjected to after coating. In one case the pin-holes allowed delamination to start which was closely followed by corrosion of the substrate metal and resulted in the replacement of the whole roof covering, some 5000 square metres. This is unlikely to be a problem with sheeting manufactured by the larger and more reputable roll forming companies which procure coated coiled sheet from identifiable and reliable sources. In the absence of national performance standards, reliance is placed on the manufacturer's quality control and testing.

7.6 Design

Respondents to our questionnaire ranked the avoidance of condensation within insulated double skin cladding constructions as the most important aspect of cladding design and 2% of reported failures related to back peel on the underside of weather sheets. The subject of interstitial condensation is addressed in Chapter 8. It is clear that owners, specifiers and contractors need a fuller understanding of moisture and air movements through and within cladding constructions for both durability and thermal performance to be achieved.

8. Problems in use

8.1 Preliminary

During the course of information gathering for this report a number of miscellaneous areas of weakness have come to light. For convenience they are collectively addressed in this Chapter as 'problems in use'. It should be noted that most of these are related to durability, although some are not. However, the problems included do represent areas of general concern as reflected in the gathered information.

8.2 Concerns

A list of concerns from questionnaire returns are given below. (See Figure 8.1.)

1. Strength of roof claddings
2. Condensation ventilation and insulation
3. Fixings
4. Thermal expansion
5. Penetrations
6. Rooflights and translucent sheeting
7. Tolerances
8. Bi-metallic corrosion
9. Handling
10. Acoustic insulation
11. Impact protection
12. Fire
13. Watertightness
14. Composite panel core adhesion.

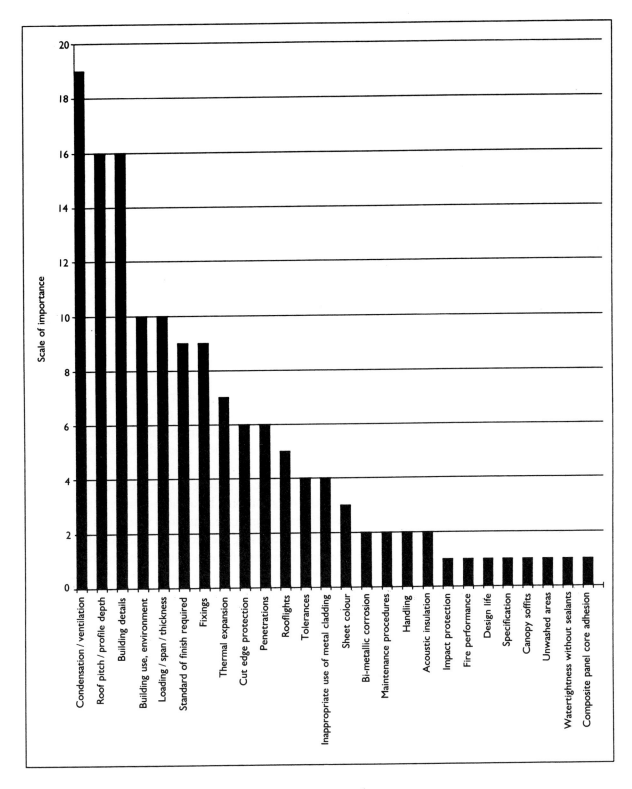

Fig. 8.1. Reported areas of concern from questionnaires returned

The problems listed above are given various degrees of importance according to how many respondents thought them important in questionnaire returns. These are illustrated in Figure 8.1. On this basis some of the most important problems are discussed below.

8.3 Strength

For profiled steel cladding, it is becoming standard practice to specify a 0.7mm thickness for roofs and 0.55mm for wall cladding. Experience has shown that if thinner roof material is used problems can arise due to foot traffic.

The strength of any profiled metal sheeting depends broadly on three major factors:

(a) Thickness of metal

(b) Material strength properties

(c) Depth of the profile

Where aluminium is used as the metal substrate, claddings tend to have lower strength since aluminium alloys have generally lower yield points than steel. This can be addressed by making profiles deeper or thickening metal substrate to achieve an equivalent strength to steel sections.

Some profiled sheet used on roofs is so weak that access onto the roof for maintenance and cleaning can only be achieved safely with the use of crawling boards. It is easy to imagine situations where this requirement is not known by persons accessing the roof, or is ignored. The result can be damage to the roof or, worse still, an accident. Damage has been seen in these situations where footprints are clearly visible from inside the roof due to the material deforming permanently under the path of persons walking on the roof. This damage can lead to breakdown of the metal protection since surface coatings may well be damaged by the uncontrolled plastic deformation of the sheeting.

The British Steel Colorcoat* guide (Ref. 25) contains succinct guidance and this is quoted below. It makes reference to BS 5427 which gives an appropriate loading for design of 0.9kN over a 125mm square area, although new European recommendations favour 1.0kN on a 100mm square.

'...the concentrated load requirement in BS 5427 (taken from CP3) is not

*Colorcoat is a regulated trademark of British Steel plc.

always appropriate for roof sheeting. How a load is applied depends to some degree on the profile shape, e.g. if a profile has, say, crowns of 25mm and valleys of 75mm, it is probable that anybody walking on the roof will step on the crowns. Walking on the crowns is unavoidable when traversing a roof of almost any profile. It follows, therefore, that at a moment in time one's entire weight plus dynamic effect could be concentrated on the width of the crown multiplied by the width of one's foot (say 100mm). Tests indicate that the dynamic force is of the order of 1.3kN for a 90kg man. [See Figure 8.2.]

To avoid damage to the sheet it should be able to resist this force on an area of crown width x 100mm applied at any position on the sheet. While it is easy to test for this condition, it is difficult to calculate the consequences. It is usual practice, therefore, to check by calculation for an equivalent line load applied normal to the direction of the profile. A value of 1.5kN/m is deemed to be sufficient. On simple, unstiffened trapezoidal profiles in Fe E220 G quality steel it is usually advisable to specify steel of 0.7mm nominal thickness to provide the necessary resistance. On stiffened trapezoidal profiles and those made from higher tensile steels it is sometimes possible to specify thinner sheets. The reader is advised to consult the profile manufacturer for guidance.'

Fig. 8.2. Loading from foot traffic

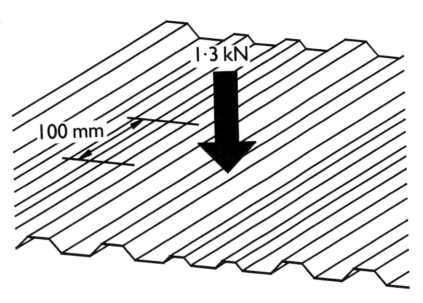

Another strength related problem concerns the widespread use of translucent sheeting on roofs. Translucent sheet is applied in rectangular panels and is an economical way of admitting overhead light to the building. To fit the metal profile sheeting surrounding it, the translucent sheet profile must be similar and certainly of the same depth. This presents a problem because translucent sheet, being generally weaker, will not normally span the distance that the profiled metal sheet will span. Hence, unless purlin spacing is reduced for the translucent sheeting the roof will be weaker in these areas, and possibly not capable of carrying the design loads. Alternatively, sheeting with load/span capacity equal to the profiled metal may be available.

8.4 Condensation

Several problems related to condensation are discussed briefly here.

Condensation arises from the variation with temperature of the capacity of air to hold moisture in the form of water vapour. As temperatures increase the capacity increases. For each temperature, however, there is a saturation level of moisture. When air which has absorbed moisture is cooled to such a temperature that the moisture content exceeds the saturation (or dew) point, the excess moisture will be deposited as water. Condensation can occur on cold surfaces or within a composite component, where it is described as interstitial condensation.

In relation to building cladding it can occur in a number of places including:

(a) Against roof sheeting

(b) At roof lights

(c) On walls

(d) Inside composite panels which are unsealed to warm air from inside the building (interstitial condensation).

Since warm air rises, the most common places to find condensation problems are in and around the roof area. Indeed, this was shown in the questionnaire returns and discussions with the users. Rooflights which are single glazed are particularly vulnerable, especially when detailed such that they actually collect warm air.

There are also several circumstances in which warm air, with a high water vapour content, can come into contact with cold wall and roof inner surfaces and so cause more serious condensation. A few are outlined below:

¤ Large areas of water within a building, for example a swimming pool where heated moist air rises to the roof area.

¤ The processes within the building which release water vapour.

¤ Gas combustion for processes or in certain types of space heating — this produces large quantities of water vapour.

¤ Warm air blowers directed at cold exterior surfaces.

¤ Moisture production within a building due to occupancy.

¤ Air conditioning systems with 'humidity' control.

There are many more examples of problem scenarios and the reader is referred to some of the standard references on the subject, for example the 'Good Practice Guide No. 61' Ref 3 or the CIBSE Guide.

Very often the designer can do little to change the amount of water vapour produced within the building and comfort levels or processes dictate temperatures and possibly humidity levels which must be maintained. However, roof design can play a large part in either promoting or preventing the occurrence of condensation. Obviously, an uninsulated roof is far more likely to have condensation on the underside of the sheeting than one which is insulated, but there are other considerations in design. Design detail drawings shown in Chapter 4 indicate that normal practice in roof design is to make the outer cladding skin a sealed rainscreen. Layers of insulation and inner lining do not normally seal against air and so warm moist air collecting in roof areas can come into contact with cold external metal cladding and cause condensation. Clearly, this could be prevented if an inner air seal was included or if the space between this and the outer rainscreen were ventilated. This is the guiding principle in the enlightened wall cladding designs which emerged in the 1960's and 1970's under the banner of the 'rainscreen principle'. So far this revolution in design has not reached the majority of insulated industrial building roofs.

Guidance from British Standards is not plentiful. Some general help is given in BS 8200, particularly Sections 11 to 21. A surface condensation prediction chart is provided in Figure 3 of that document.

The consequences of condensation can be serious. Some examples are given below:

1. Corrosion at end laps of sheet. Condensate running down the inside of a roof or wall sheet is arrested at an end lap where a series of drips are formed. These, in time, cause corrosion of unprotected sheet edges.

2. Corrosion of fixings (see Photograph 10). Again, condensate is arrested by the fixing where it passes through the cladding and water accumulates due to surface tension effects. If the fixing material is not chosen carefully then galvanic action may cause corrosion of the fixing. Also, corrosion at the hole through the sheet

material is a possibility since these holes are normally left unprotected.

3. Staining to wall finishes such as plasterboard and the sheet material itself where water run marks can be seen.

4. Discomfort factor of having pools of condensate, large or small, collecting at points in the building.

5. Mould growth.

6. Risk of wet rot, dry rot and insect attack in timbers.

7. Accumulation of dirt on wet surfaces.

To summarise, problems do occur but design remedies can be found which reduce the risk of condensation or eliminate it altogether.

8.5 Fixings

Much has already been said on the subject of fixings and so it is sufficient here simply to list the concerns:

1. Corrosion of roof sheet at and around fixing holes (discussed briefly in Section 8.2).

2. Corrosion of fixings due to condensate and rainwater run-off.

3. Staining from fixings. This can be either corrosion product carried down the face by rainwater or accumulations of dirt around fixings again being carried down the face.

4. Coloured snap-on caps deteriorating, cracking and falling off. This often leaves fixings vulnerable to corrosion and the staining mentioned above.

5. Distortion of fixing holes in sheet and/or fixings due to expansion and contraction of the cladding sheet. Many designers place reliance on flexibility of the fixings to allow for thermal movement and building movement. The problems become more pronounced with the use of longer sheets and again with the use of aluminium which has a greater coefficient of linear expansion than steel.

8.6 Thermal expansion problem

This has already been referred to above in Section 8.3 on fixings.

A range of service temperatures is given in Table 8.1. This is taken from CIRIA Technical Note 107 1981. It must be noted that whilst BS 8200 gives air temperature ranges for the external environment, these do not include the effects of solar gain on surfaces as the figures in Table 8.1 do.

Table 8.1. Temperature ranges for cladding

	Minimum °C	Maximum °C	Range °C
External Cladding, walling, roofing			
Heavyweight			
light colour	−20	50	70
dark colour	−20	65	85
Lightweight, over insulation			
light colour	−25	60	85
dark colour	−25	80	105
Glass			
coloured or solar control	−25	90	115
clear	−25	40	65
Fully exposed structural members			
Concrete			
light colour	−20	45	65
dark colour	−20	60	80
Metal			
light colour	−25	50	75
dark colour	−25	65	90
Internal Normal use	10	30	20
Empty/out of use	−5	35	40

The CIRIA document continues with the following observation:

'Whereas the total temperature range is important, the variations from the temperature at installation or datum temperature are often more important. Performance of joints between cladding panels or in structural slabs depends on the range above or below the datum. It is unlikely that this datum would vary outside the range +5 to +25C, and a smaller range may be appropriate in many cases. However, some allowance for solar gain may need to be made for sensitive cladding panels.'

The last sentence is particularly valid for coated metal claddings. Using the above table and installation temperature range it can be seen that the following overall changes in temperature (°C) from installation are possible:

Positive	+5 to +80	75°C
		(causing expansion)
Negative	+25 to -25	50°C
		(causing contraction)

These temperatures are for dark colours, which absorb more heat from the sun, over insulation which helps to prevent that heat from escaping. Lesser ranges are applicable to uninsulated cladding and light colours. However, it can be seen that metal claddings, which by definition are lightweight, need to be designed to cater for fairly large movements.

For example, a 5m sheet in steel:

¤ Expansion up to 4.5mm

¤ Contraction up to 3.0mm

and these figures for aluminium sheet are:

¤ Expansion up to 9.0mm

¤ Contraction up to 6.0mm.

This is a total movement of 15mm and must be accommodated by the fixings. Proper consideration of this must be given in the design and it may well be that with standard fixing types and design data in tabular form the problem of thermal movement of the cladding can be overcome. These figures are similar to those contained in BS 5427 : 1976 but the advice given there on accommodating movement needs revision to account for current fixing methods.

8.7 Water penetration

The science and mechanism of water penetration have been known for many years. An excellent guidance document is the AAMA 'Aluminium curtain wall design guide manual' (see Ref. 26). Despite its title it has much that is relevant to coated metal cladding design in both aluminium and steel.

Fundamentally, it explains the forces that cause water to penetrate a cladding using the well known six categories. These are based on the early papers on the subject. BS 8200, Section 33 on the other hand is not clear on the mechanisms and is thus in need of revision.

Good wall and roof design prevent water penetration from occurring, but when it does occur this can be due to several reasons:

¤ Inadequate sealing details on walls.

¤ Inadequate drainage and ventilation of walls.

¤ Insufficient falls on roofs. Water can be driven back up the slope by wind action.

¤ Expansion of roof sheet breaking sealant joints between sheet laps and so admitting rainwater.

¤ Leaking through fixing holes or through holes drilled but not used for fixing.

¤ Insufficient lap lengths, particularly for roof claddings.

It can be seen that only some of these problems relate to site construction and that design guidance is an important key.

9. Discussion and conclusions

1. Cladding manufacture is a long process, often with several separate companies involved. This gives rise to increased opportunity for defects in the finished product.

2. There is no British Standard for coil coating and roll forming. In assessing the quality of the finished product, purchasers rely on the reputation of the manufacturer.

3. Plastisol has proved to be the workhorse coating for UK industrial buildings. Failures reported to manufacturers within the manufacturers' stated product life probably amount to between 0.25% and 0.5% of area installed for the UK produced materials. The position has improved in recent years with new formulations becoming available. It must be remembered though that actual failure rates will be higher since not all are reported.

4. Cut edge corrosion has always been an issue with organically coated metal sheet. Many cladding manufacturers claimed it to be generally associated with site cut edges. However, evidence gathered during this study suggests that much of the cut edge corrosion is also occurring at factory cut edges.

   Site painting of all cut edges is recommended by some industry professionals but is difficult to achieve in practice. As a result it is not normally done. There is no generally accepted solution to this problem in existence at the present time.

5. Delamination continues to be a significant mode of failure for Plastisol coatings. As much as 70% of reported failures of early Plastisol formulations were attributed to delamination; with later formulations the figure dropped to 24%. This reflects improvements in manufacturing processes as well as coating formulation.

6. The majority of failures with early formulations of Plastisol occurred on wall cladding, current figures show that failures predominantly occur on roofs. It is probable that the data are influenced by the considerable increase in use of coated metal cladding for roofs after the demise of asbestos cement as a roof material and also by the

trend towards lower roof pitch.

7. Much of the available data on failures in the UK originates from or relates to British materials. The data presented in this study, however, includes failures of materials from all sources including imported materials. It has not been possible to identify failures of imported materials in isolation. However, figures from all sources indicate 42% of failures for Plastisol are due to delamination compared with only 24% for British material, suggesting a quality differential between material sources in this respect.

8. The need to consider condensation and to design cladding constructions which limit its formation is seen by many as the most important area of concern.

9. The rapid removal of water from the surface of cladding is important to its long term performance. This relates in particular to roofs. Design guidance on detailing, minimum roof slopes, sealing etc. is in need of further development and dissemination within the industry.

10. The table of reported areas of concern (Figure 8.1) reflects the development of the profiled metal sheet industry. All areas referred to can give performance difficulties, those with a low incidence of referral are thought to have been largely addressed by the industry.

11. The good quality cladding materials have a relatively low rate of failure.

12. General design guidance documents have, to date, included the following, some of which are in common use:

1968 Constrado (Ref. 13)	*Profiled Steel cladding and decking for commercial and industrial buildings.*
1982 NFRC (Ref. 2)	*Profiled sheet metal roofing and cladding. A guide to good practice.*
1983 Constrado/ ECCS (Ref. 10)	*Good practice in steel cladding and roofing.*
1991 (Ref. 5)	*Industrial roofing and cladding.*
1992 MCRMA (Ref. 24)	*Design guides.*

1993 British Steel **(Ref. 25)**	*Colourcoat in building.*
1993 BRE (Ref. 3)	*Good practice guide 61 design manual.*

It is concluded that whilst these documents and others do provide some guidance for manufacturers, designers, specifiers, contractors and users of cladding, there are anomalies, differences in advice and areas where more work is needed for an in-depth understanding. A comprehensive design guidance document is needed. Clearly, this is not available at present in one reference document and hence obtaining information can be difficult.

13. British Standards need updating and a new Standard is needed for the manufacture and testing of coated metal cladding.

Appendix

Checklist for specifiers

The following is an aide-memoir for anyone considering the use of organic coated metal sheet cladding.

Designers and specifiers should ensure their requirements are met in each subject area.

Design Life
Site environment
Loading (including wind)
Required spans
Roof pitch
Cladding material (steel, aluminium etc.)
Steel type
Galvanise weight
Sheet thickness
Flashing and trim thicknesses
Thermal expansion
Acoustic insulation
Coating type and colour
Colour stability
Evidence of suitability

U value
Interstitial condensation
Side lap sealant
End lap sealant
Fixings — type, washers, colour caps, fixing centres
Rooflights — grade, thickness, site sealed, factory sealed
Fire and surface spread of flame ratings
Penetration soakers
Building and material tolerances
Impact protection
Site test requirements
Packaging, handling, storage and protection requirements

Design details

Manufacturers of profiled metal cladding normally offer a range of flashings to complement their systems together with construction details to show how their whole system fits together. The following details are not based on any one particular source but are drawn from our experience and offered as indicative examples only. They represent the normal standard of design detailing currently in use in the UK and are not offered with any recommendation.

Fig. A1. Eaves detail

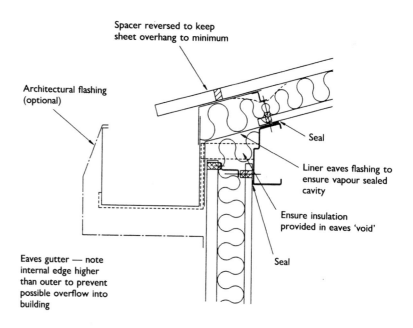

Spacer reversed to keep
sheet overhang to minimum

Architectural flashing
(optional)

Seal

Liner eaves flashing to
ensure vapour sealed
cavity

Ensure insulation
provided in eaves 'void'

Seal

Eaves gutter — note
internal edge higher
than outer to prevent
possible overflow into
building

Fig. A2. Window or door head

Space sheets off
drip flashing

Fig. A3. Gable detail

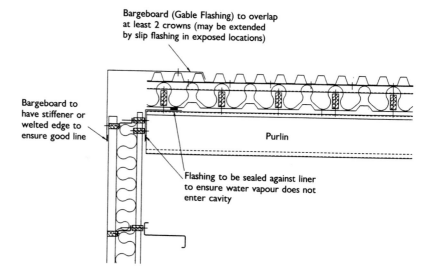

Bargeboard (Gable Flashing) to overlap
at least 2 crowns (may be extended
by slip flashing in exposed locations)

Bargeboard to
have stiffener or
welted edge to
ensure good line

Purlin

Flashing to be sealed against liner
to ensure water vapour does not
enter cavity

Fig. A4. Side wall adjoining roof slope

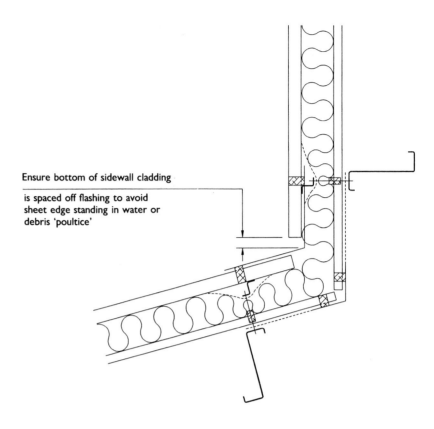

Ensure bottom of sidewall cladding

is spaced off flashing to avoid sheet edge standing in water or debris 'poultice'

Fig. A5. Ridge detail

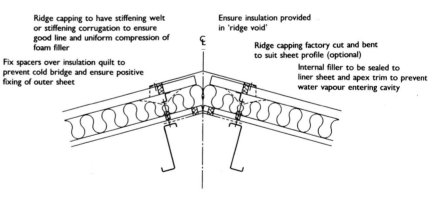

Ridge capping to have stiffening welt or stiffening corrugation to ensure good line and uniform compression of foam filler

Fix spacers over insulation quilt to prevent cold bridge and ensure positive fixing of outer sheet

Ensure insulation provided in 'ridge void'

Ridge capping factory cut and bent to suit sheet profile (optional)

Internal filler to be sealed to liner sheet and apex trim to prevent water vapour entering cavity

Fig. A6. Ridge detail

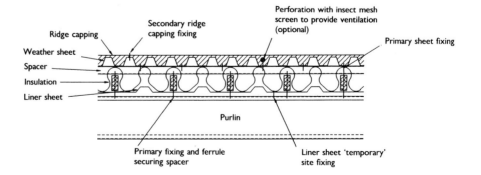

Ridge capping
Weather sheet
Spacer
Insulation
Liner sheet

Secondary ridge capping fixing

Perforation with insect mesh screen to provide ventilation (optional)

Primary sheet fixing

Purlin

Primary fixing and ferrule securing spacer

Liner sheet 'temporary' site fixing

List of contact organisations

Organisation:	Architectural Advisory Service Centre
Address:	Spendale House The Runway South Ruislip Middlesex HA4 6SJ
Organisation:	ALFED (Aluminium Federation)
Address:	Broadway House Calthorpe Road Birmingham B15 1TN
Organisation:	Architectural Aluminium Association
Address:	11 Cleeve Cloud Lane Prestbury Cheltenham Gloucestershire GL52 5SE
Organisation:	Building Research Establishment
Address:	Garston Watford WD2 7JR
Organisation:	Centre for Window and Cladding Technology
Address:	University of Bath Claverton Down Bath BA2 7AY

Organisation: CIRIA

Address: 6 Storey's Gate
                 Westminster
                 London
                 SW1P 3AU

Organisation: European Coil Coaters Association

Address: 32 Swansea Road
                 Penllergaer
                 Swansea
                 West Glamorgan
                 SA4 1AQ

Organisation: Metal Cladding and Roofing Manufacturers Association

Address: 18 Mere Farm Road
                 Noctorum
                 Birkenhead
                 Merseyside
                 L43 9TT

Organisation: National Federation of Roofing Contractors

Address: 24 Weymouth Street
                 London
                 W1N 3FA

Organisation: NBA Building Performance Services

Address: Grosvenor House
                 141–143 Drury Lane
                 London
                 WC2B 5TS

Organisation: Paint Research Association

Address: 8 Waldegrave Road
                 Teddington
                 Middlesex
                 TW11 8LD

Organisation: WS Atkins

Address: Woodcote Grove
                 Ashley Road
                 Epsom
                 Surrey
                 KT18 5BW

References

1. Kempster J.A., Bassi R., Performance Survey of organic coated roof sheeting, BRE (limited circulation), March 1993.

2. Profiled Sheet Metal Roofing & Cladding - a guide to good practice, 2nd Edition, The National Federation of Roofing Contractors, September 1991.

3. Building Research Establishment, Good Practice Guide - Design Manual February 1993.

4. Colourcoat in Building - Model Specification and Product Selector, British Steel Strip Products, March 1993.

5. Spacey D.B., Industrial Roofing & Cladding, IRC, 1991.

6. CEA, UK Corrosion 89 Blackpool 8-10 November Vol. 2, CEA, 1989.

7. RIBA, Conferences on Avoiding Building Failure, RIBA, 1990.

8. Colourcoat Inspection and Maintenance Manual, British Steel Strip Products, May 1992.

9. 2 Day Symposium on Protection & Maintenance of Building Materials, May 89.

10. ECCS, Good Practice in Steel Cladding and Roofing, Constrado, May 1983.

11. The Design of Profiled Sheeting, Constrado, 1984.

12. Wieland H., Corrosion problems in roofing and siding, SFS, October 1988.

13. BSC Strip Mill Products, Profiled Steel Cladding and Decking for Commercial and Industrial Buildings, Constrado, 1968.

14. Landolfo R., Mazzolani F.M., Behaviour of Third Generation Trapezoidal Steel Sheetings Confereince: Testing of Metals for Structures, Naples, Italy, 29-31 May 1990, E. & F.N. Spon, 1992.

15. Tsai T., Crisinel M., Moment Redistribution in Profiled Sheeting, Eight International Speciality Conference on Cold-formed Steel Structures, St Louis, MO, USA, 11-12 Nov 1986, University of Missouri - Rolla, Rolla, MO, USA, 1986.

16. Turner A., Steel Roofing - the importance of fasteners, Joining & Materials v. 2 n.8 Aug 1989 p 384-385, 1989.

17. Asher J.M.B., Repaint Systems for Cladding, Sheet Met. ind. v.61, p 285-286, 288, May 1984.

18. Skelly J.T., Clad Metals: Design for Corrosion Control and Performance, Metal Progress v. 124 n.3 p 35-38, Aug 1983.

19. Davies J.M., Design Criteria for Structural Sandwich Panels, Structural Engineer, Part A v. 65 n.12 p 435-441, Dec 1987.

20. Brookes A., Hampton J., Precoated Metal Cladding, Architects' Journal, 1985, v.181 n.16.

21. Bryan E., Design of Profiled Steel Sheeting & Decking 1984.

22. Josey B., Element Design Guide, External Walls. Part 4: Profiled Metal Sheet, Architects' Journal, v.184 n.31 p 33-38, 40, 30 July 1986.

23. Davies J.M., Profiled Steel Cladding, Consulting Engineer, v.44 n.2, p 24-25, 27-28, 1980.

24. The Metal Cladding & Roofing Manufacturers Association Ltd, Design Guides 1992.

25. British Steel Strip Production, Colourcoat in Building - A Guide to Architectural Practice, BSSP, March 1993.

26. The Architectural Aluminium Manufacturers Association, Aluminium Curtain Wall Design Guide Manual, 1979.

Bibliography

Ref. no.	Title	Author	Publisher	Date of publication
1	Steel–Frames, Flooring, Cladding	JC Taylor		1985
2	Classified Maintenance Inspection	CWJ Bos		
3	Fitted Sheets	M Coomber		1993
4	Coated Steel Cladding	T Andrew		1982
5	Wall Cladding Defects & Their Diagnosis	BRE	BRE	1978
6	British Steel Strip Products: Galvatite Technical Manual		BS	1993
7	British Steel Strip Products: Zalutite Zinc/Aluminium Alloy Coated Steel		BS	1993
8	Maintaining & Improving Steel Houses	Finch	BRE	1987
9	British Steel Product Development Centre: White Rust on Galvanised Steel	TO Andrew	BS	1993
10	European Recommendations for Steel Construction: Good Practice in Steel Cladding & roofing		ECCS ECCS	1983 1983
11	Syntha Pulvin: Trade Literature		Synth Pulvin	1993
12	Roofs & Roofing — New materials, industrial applications, uses & performance	May		
13	Construction & Building Materials Vol 2	DM Howell		1988
14	One Day Training Workshop for Building Surveyors — Metal Cladding	DM Howell		1991
15	Profiled Sheet Steel Roofs & Internal Humidity	B Steel		
16	National Coil Coaters Association 1985 Annual Meeting	DM Howell		1985
17	Colorcoat & Stevitite Pre-finished Steel – Technical Manual	B Steel		
18	Preliminary European Recommendation for Sandwich Panels: Part I Design		ECCS	1991
19	Preliminary European Recommendation for Sandwich Panels: Part II Good Practice		ECCS	1990
20	Cladding Methods in New Zealand	AJ Brookes	BRANZ	1984
21	Nail-Sheet Interaction of Corrugated Sheet Steel Cladding	TP Neal	BRANS	1985
22	Dampness in Pitched Industrial Roofs		BRE	1988
23	The Testing of Profiled Metal Sheets		Constrado	1984
24	The Design & Testing of Connections in Steel Sheeting & Sections		Constrado	1983
25	Colour Coated Profiled Cladding	NW Hill	WS Atkins	1984
26	Colour Coated Profiled Metal Cladding Materials	WS Atkins	WS Atkins	1981
27	Structural Survey		HSP	1991
28	Colour Coated Profiled Building Cladding	WS Atkins	WS Atkins	1979
29	Steel Framed & Steel Clad Houses: Inspection & Assessment		BRE	1987
30	Pre-Coated Metal Cladding For Building	DM Bishop		
31	The Renovation of Painted Metallic Facades	EV Schmid		

Ref. no.	Title	Author	Publisher	Date of publication
32	Corrosion Test For Coil Coated Sheet In Atmosphere Containing SO_2		ECCA	
33	Metal Skinned Sandwich Panels for External Walls	RP Thorogood	BRE	1976
34	Weathering of Latex Paints on Galvanised Sheet Roofing		BRENZ	1975
35	Mechanical Fasteners For Use In Steel Sheeting & Sections		Constrado	1983
36	Architectural Powder Coatings	M Osmond		1991
37	A study of the Relationships…	K Johnson		1987
38	Building Deck Waterproofing	L Gish	ASTM	1989
39	Composite Steel Structures	K Narayanan		1987
40	Delamination & Remedial Repair of GFRC Cladding Panels	FJ Krishan	ASCE	1986
41	Testing of Profiled Metal Sheeting	R Baehre	E&FN	1992
42	Standing Seam — Best Bet For Metals in Roofing		Modern Metals	1985
43	Painted Metals — Architectural Use Grows	J Schrants		1987
44	Crafting the Custom Sheet Metal Roof	S Cechvala		1989
45	Roof Failures & How to Void Them	D Adler		1989
46	The Design of Fixings For Cladding		Constr Repair	1989
47	Specifying Standard Seam Roofing Systems For Conventional Buildings	J Taylor		1986
48	Standard Seam Metal Roofs in Retrofit	D Perry		1986
49	Coil Coating — Changing Perspectives	N Makins		1985
50	Load Deformation Characteristics & Design Loads of Screw Fastenings	D Masse		1989
51	Metal Cladding Envelope Problems, Retrofit Solutions	A Colantonio		1992
52	Corrosion & Corrosion Prevention in Exterior Metal Cladding	J Duncan		1985
53	Roofing: Coated Coils Next Growth Market	F Church		1987
54	Analytical Studies of Building Cladding	B Goodno		1986
55	Coated Coil Flaunt Product Design Versatility	M Cassidy		1984
56	Clad Metals — Methods For Economy	W Cote		1984
57	Aluminium Zinc Coated Steel	H Townsend		1986
58	Clad Metals — Material Conservation Through — Design For Corrosion Control and High Performance	J Skelly		1983
59	Cost Benefit Analysis of Aluminium Roofing Sheets	G Kalra		1986
60	Condensation Under Metal Sheeted Roofs	M Kelly		1973
61	Design of Foam Filled Composite Panels	J Davies		1987
62	Metal Industrial Roofs Moisture Problems	P Falconer		1986
63	Coating For Galvanised Steel in Industrial Buildings	A Clothier		1981
64	Failure of Sheet Metal Roofing Under Repeated Wind Loads	J Morgan		1977
65	Steel Sheets Come Coloured			1965
66	The Changing Role of Coatings in The Building Industry	P Whitley		1979
67	Use of Zinc Coated Steel as Building Panels & Roofing Material in Agricultural Application	M Kim		
68	Weathering Steel Cladding Failures	J Frauenhoffer		1987
69	Testing of Profiled Metal Sheeting	R Baehre		1992
70	Specification Improvements For Steel & Cladding		PSA	1987
71	Plastic Coated Steel Cladding Answers its critics	A Maysmith		1986

Ref. no.	Title	Author	Publisher	Date of publication
72	Push Test on Studs Welded Through Profiled Steel Sheeting	J Mottram RG Vise		1990
73	Pre-Painted Strip For The Building & Construction Industry: Products & Performance	JM Sketchley		
74	An Assessment of Coil Coated Cladding Sheets for Coastal Power Station Construction	E Bodnar/ H Alfort		
75	European Experience With Polyester Powder Coatings For Aluminium Extrusion	E Bodnor		
76	Development of Polyester Powder Coating Systems for Outdoor Architectural Application	DSD Norwood		
77	The Benefits & Use of Powder Coatings for Architectural Aluminium	GC Bellens		
78	Properties & Performance of Styrene Based Systems on Metallic Cladding Panels			
79	Field Study & Accelerated Weathering of Coil Coated Sheet Metal	C Sjostrom		
80	European Coil Coating Review, Building On Coil Coating	ECC Review		
81	European Coil Coating Review, ECCA Eurodes	PJ Franck S Jacques		
82	Performance Requirements For Powder Coatings Used in Architectural Claddings and Extrusions			
83	Architectural Powder Coatings: A Review Of New Advances In Exterior Durable Systems	MF Osmond		
84	Accelerated Outdoor Weathering Tests For Evaluating The Durability Of Coatings	MP Moorse	BRE	1993
85	Profiled Metal Sheeting			
86	Powder Coating For Post Form Application	JW Ainsworth	SFS	
87	Drying-Out Of Saturated Flat Roof Structures	R Schubert	SFS	
88	Corrosion of Fasteners in Low Sloped Roofing Systems Installed Over Steel Decking	H Wieland	SFS	
89	Heat Conduction & Condensation Precipitation by Fasteners of Metal or Plastics in Non-ventilated Roof Assemblies	H Wieland	SFS	
90	AASC Metal Finishing Specification NBS Format	J Martin	AASC	1993
91	Austenitic Stainless Steel Fasteners: Why You Can't Afford To Gamble		SFS	1991
92	Fastening Systems For Roofing & Cladding Applications: Spedec S Self-Drilling & Fasteners		SFS	
93	Coated & Profiled Steel Sheet as Building Element For Walls	D Hancke		1974
94	European Recommendations For The Testing (Structural) of Profiled Metal Sheets		ECCS	1977
95	Japanese Industrial Standard: Polyvinyl Chloride-Metal Laminated Sheets		Jap Stan Assoc	1973
96	Aluminium Profiled Sheet Roofing Failure Cladding		Feedback Digest	
97	Specifications & Other Lit From European Coil Coating Association		ECCA	1984
98	Paint Specification For International Paints		Int Paints	
99	Report on Galvanised Sheeting to Firewall Panels	D Howell	WS Atkins	1985
100	Aluminium Cladding In Power Station Construction	EW Skerrey	BACO	

Ref. no.	Title	Author	Publisher	Date of publication
101	Prepainted Aluminium For The Building Industry A Comparison Of Coating Performance	DJ Sibley	Alcan Booth	
102	The Use of PVC Plastisole in Coil Coating	S Palminger		
103	Degradation Of Long-Life Fluoropolymer Coatings: Technical Report	JB Edwards	PRA	1976
104	Dungeness Cladding Exposure Tests	WS Atkins	WS Atkins	1981
105	Photographs of Wall Cladding Drax Completion	WS Atkins	WS Atkins	1979
106	Performance Tests on Colour Coated Industrial Building Cladding	WS Atkins	WS Atkins	1980
107	Instructions & Specification For Repainting & Overpainting BS Plastisol	WS Atkins	WS Atkins	1991
108	Curtain Wall Connections to Steel Frames		SCI	1992
109	Overcladding of Existing Buildings		SCI	1992
110	Standard & Guide to Good Practice For Curtain Walling		CWCT	1993

List of Standards related to coated metal cladding

ASTM B117	Standard test method of salt spray testing
ASTM D522	Standard test method for mandrel bend test of attached organic coatings
ASTM D523	Standard test method for specular gloss
ASTM D610	Standard test method for evaluating degree of rusting on painted steel surfaces
ASTM D660	Standard test method for evaluating degree of checking of exterior paints
ASTM D661	Standard test method for evaluating degree of cracking of exterior paints
ASTM D714	Standard test method for evaluating degree of blistering of paints
ASTM D772	Standard test method for evaluating degree of flaking (sealing) of exterior paints
ASTM D968	Standard test method for abrasion resistance of organic coatings by falling abrasive
ASTM D1400	Standard test method for nondestructive measurement of dry film thickness of nonconductive coatings applied to non ferrous metal base
ASTM D2244	Standard test method for calculations of colour differences from instrumentally measured colour coordinates

ASTM D2248	Standard practice for detergent resistance of organic finishes
ASTM D2794	Standard test method for resistance of organic coatings to the effects of rapid deformation (impact)
ASTM D3363	Standard test method for film hardness by pencil test
ASTM D4060	Standard test method for abrasion resistance of organic coatings by the Taber abraser
BS 476	Fire tests on building materials and structures
BS 690	Asbestos-cement slates and sheets (in several parts)
BS 729	Specification for hot dip galvanised coatings on iron and steel articles
BS 849	Code of practice for plain sheet zinc roofing
BS 1091	Specification for pressed steel gutters, rain water pipes, fittings and accessories
BS 1178	Specification for milled lead sheet for building purposes
BS 1282	Guide to the choice, use and application of wood preservatives
BS 1449	Steel plate, sheet and strip (in several parts and sections)
BS 1470	Specification wrought aluminium and aluminium alloys for general engineering purposes; plate, sheet and strip
BS 1494	Specification for fixing accessories for building purposes
BS 2782	Methods of testing plastics
BS 2989	Specification for continuously hot-dip zinc coated and iron-zinc alloy coated steel flat products: tolerances on dimensions and shape

BS 3083	Specification for hot-dip zinc coated and hot-dip aluminium/zinc coated corrugated steel sheets for general purposes
BS 3900	Methods of test for paints
BS 3987	Specification for anodic oxidation coatings on wrought aluminium for external architectural applications
BS 4154	Specification for profiles and dimensions
BS 4203	Extruded rigid PVC corrugated sheeting
BS 4315	Methods of test for resistance to air and water penetration
BS 4800	Schedule of paint colours for building purpose
BS 4842	Stoving organic finishes on aluminium extrusions and pre-formed sections for external architectural applications
BS 4868	Specification for profiled aluminium sheet for building
BS 4904	Specification for external cladding colours for building purposes
BS 5250	The control of condensation in dwellings Code of practice for control of condensation in buildings
BS 5427	Code of practice for performance and loading criteria for profiled sheeting in building
BS 5493	Code of practice for protective coating of iron and steel structures against corrosion
BS 6100	Glossary of building and civil engineering terms
BS 6150	Code of Practice for painting of buildings
BS 6262	Code of practice for glazing for buildings

BS 6496	Specification for powder organic coatings for application and stoving to aluminium alloy extrusion, sheet and pre-formed sections for external architecture purposes, and for the finish on aluminium alloy extrusion, sheet and pre-formed sections coated with powder organic coatings
BS 6497	Specification for power organic coatings for application and stoving hot-dip galvanised hot-rolled steel sections and pre-formed steel sheet for windows and associated external architectural purposes, and for the finish on galvanised steel sections and pre-formed sheet coated with powder organic coatings
BS 6687	Specification for electrolytically zinc coated steel flat rolled products
BS 6830	Specification for continuously hot-dip aluminium/zinc alloy coated cold rolled carbon steel flat products
BS 8200	Code of practice for design of non-loadbearing external vertical enclosures of buildings
CP 143	Code of Practice for sheet roof and wall coverings
DIN 4102	Fire behaviour of building materials and building components
DIN 16937	(PVC-P) waterproofing sheet compatible with bitumen requirements
DIN 55928	Corrosion protection of steel structures by organic, inorganic and metallic coating or metallic coatings; general concepts and corrosion loads
BS EN 10002	Tensile testing of metallic materials
BS EN 10142	Specification for continuously hot-dip zinc coated for low carbon steel sheet and strip for cold forming: technical delivery conditions
BS EN 10147	Specification for continuously hot-dip zinc coated structural steel sheet and strip: technical delivery conditions
* DD24	Recommendation for methods of protection against corrosion on light

section steel used in building

ISO 174	Plastics: Determination of viscosity number of PVC resins in dilute solution
ISO 683/13	Heat-treatable steels, alloy steels and free cutting steels — wrought stainless steel
ISO 1459	Metallic coatings: Protection against corrosion by hot dip galvanizing-guiding principles
ISO 1460	Metallic coatings: Hot dip galvanised coatings on ferrous metals materials — gravimetric determination of the mass per unit area
ISO 1461	Metallic coatings: Hot dip galvanised coating on fabricated ferrous products — Requirements
ISO 3575	Continuous hot-dip zinc-coating of carbon steel sheet of commercial, lock forming and drawing qualities
ISO 6361	Wrought aluminium and aluminium alloy sheets strips and plates – technical conditions for inspection and delivery
ISO 6892	Metallic materials — Tensile testing
ISO 8618	Plastics — Liquid phenolic resins — Determination of non-volatile matter

Continuous hot-dp zinc-coating of carbon steel sheet at commercial, lock forming and drawing qualities

* DD — Draft for Development

Glossary of terms

Acrylic   Organic coating. Thermosetting and thermoplastic acrylic copolymers.

Back peel   The physical state where the organic coatings on the reverse (non-exposed) side of a cladding sheet detach from the metal substrate.

Breather membrane   A layer of vapour-permeable material laid on the cold side of the insulation to protect the insulation from the effects of moisture on the underside of the external sheet.

Blistering   A defect in composite panels where the panel skin becomes detached from the insulation core over an area of the panel, usually protruding in a curved or domed fashion.

Chalking   The powder product of coating deterioration in particular due to solar radiation.

Cinch strap   A panel strap used in some secret fix systems to reinforce the end lap with a backing plate.

Cladding   The external envelope of the building which normally carries no loads beyond its own weight, those imposed by snow and wind, and those that occur during maintenance.

Clip   An aluminium or steel bracket used in secret fix systems attaching one, two or three ribs to a separate spacer system or to the structure.

Colour change   A change in colour from the original due to weathering. Can be calibrated using ASTM Standard Test Method D2244-89. A test procedure is referred to in BS 3900 : Part D1.

Composite panel   A cladding sheet with insulation bonded to it. Sandwich panels are sometimes referred to as composite panels.

Cover width   The distance covered by an individual cladding sheet when laid in multiples.

Creep	The tendency for sandwich panels to suffer increasing deflection with time as a consequence of viscous flow in the core material.
Crown	The top face of the rib.
Delamination	The physical state where organic coatings detach from the metal substrate.
Depth	The distance from the top of the crown to the bottom of the valley from the front face of the profile.
Double skin cladding	A roof or wall covering combining a profiled exterior sheet covering an interior board or sheet lining, with insulation and spacers between the two. Also, known as a 'built-up wall system'.
Fastener	An item used to attach cladding to the supporting frame or to seal the cladding sheets together.
Filiform corrosion	A linear form of corrosion which progresses under a surface coating in a random direction. Often initiated in a salt laden environment, it is self perpetuating. It does not usually affect material strength since the depth of corrosion is very small.
Flashing	A flat metal sheet having the same coatings as the cladding and bent to shape to form junction connections at the positions where areas of cladding change shape or direction, for example at eaves of the building and at openings.
Flute closure or foam filler	Profiled strips, usually of plastic foam, rubber or mineral fibre, for sealing the sheeting and preventing bird or rodent entry at flashing positions.
Gloss change	A reduction in the amount of incident light reflected at a surface.
Halter	An extruded aluminium bracket used in secret fix systems providing function of spacer between liner and weathering sheet and of anchorage against uplift.
HP200	British Steel Plastisol formulation.
Organic coating	An organic chemistry based formulation applied to steel or aluminium sheet to give a colour finish and to enhance weather protection.
Pitch	The distance between any repeated portion of the profile.

Plastisol	Thermoplastic organic coating containing PVC resin in plastiser. Formulations are available from various paint companies.
Polyvinylidene-fluoride (PVF2 or PVDF)	Organic coating developed by Penwalt Corporation, USA, and formulated under licence in the UK. Fluorine is introduced into PVC to produce the fluorocarbon.
Power coating	A coating applied as a powder to an electrostatically charged metal object. The coating is then heated to first fuse then cure it to form a hard covering.
Profile	The cross-sectional shape of a cladding sheet.
Rib	The portion of the profile that protrudes.
Roll forming	The process by which flat sheet is passed between a series of rollers which yield the sheet to form the chosen profile.
Sandwich panel	Roof or wall cladding panel in the form of a sandwich in which the inner and outer faces are formed from thin metal sheets and the core is a relatively low strength material having stiffening and insulating properties.
Secondary fastener	A secondary fastener attaches one sheet to another, to flashings and to cappings. They are used to ensure close contact between sheets and any compressible sealant.
Secret fix roofing	A self supporting metal profile with virtually no through fixings. Variously expressed as concealed fixing, standing seam, clip fix or raised seam.
Siding	Wall cladding.
Silicon modified polyester	Organic coating. Silicon modified version of resins derived from synthetic materials.
Stiffener	A change in profile across the width of a crown, valley or web.
Syntha Pulvin	Organic coating. A polyester powder coating electrostatically sprayed and heat cured.
Trapezoidal sheeting	Profiled sheeting in which the ribs form the shape of a trapezium in cross section.
Trough	The portion of the profile that recedes.

Valley   The bottom face of the trough.

Vapour barrier   A layer of impervious material laid on the warm side of the insulation to prevent the transmission of moisture into the insulation.

Web   The angled walls of the profile rib.